THE GREAT TRANSFORMATION

CLIMATE — CAN WE BEAT THE HEAT?

Idea and concept:
Alexandra Hamann, Claudia Zea-Schmidt,
Reinhold Leinfelder

Scenario:
Alexandra Hamann and Claudia Zea-Schmidt

Scientific advisor:
Reinhold Leinfelder

Graphics:
Jörg Hartmann, Jörg Hülsmann,
Robert Nippoldt, Studio Nippoldt, Iris Ugurel

WBGU

This project would not have been possible without the generous assistance and
voluntary cooperation of members of the
German Advisory Council on Global Change (WBGU).

The prologue was drawn by Iris Ugurel (Berlin).
Hans Joachim Schellnhuber, Dirk Messner and Renate Schubert were drawn
by Robert Nippoldt (Münster).
Reinhold Leinfelder, Jürgen Schmid and Sabine Schlacke were drawn
by Jörg Hülsmann (Berlin).
Stefan Rahmstorf, Nebojša Nakićenović, Claus Leggewie and the spectacular finale were drawn
by Jörg Hartmann (Münster).
The cover art is the work of Studio Nippoldt
(Astrid Nippoldt, Christine Goppel and Robert Nippoldt).
Translation by Bob Culverhouse (Berlin).
Editorial management and scientific advice by WBGU Secretariat (Berlin).
Special thanks for proofreading go to Vincenzo Zambrano (Toronto, Canada).

This project was supported by the German Federal Ministry for Education and Research within the
framework of the Science Year 2012 – Project EARTH: Our Future. It is based on the study *World in
Transition – A Social Contract for Sustainability* published by the WBGU in 2011.

Free copies of the comic-book can
be ordered from
www.wbgu.de

Content

PROLOGUE

PRECAMBRIAN, ABOUT THREE BILLION YEARS AGO

LIVING ROCKS: PRESENT-DAY STROMATOLITES IN SHARK BAY,
WESTERN AUSTRALIA. IN THE PRECAMBRIAN THEY WERE
SPREAD ALL OVER THE WORLD.

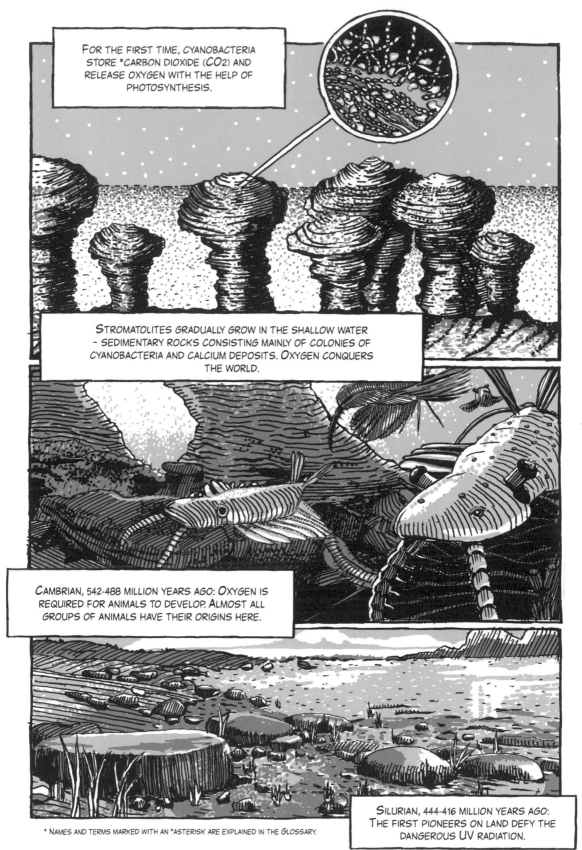

FOR THE FIRST TIME, CYANOBACTERIA STORE *CARBON DIOXIDE (CO_2) AND RELEASE OXYGEN WITH THE HELP OF PHOTOSYNTHESIS.

STROMATOLITES GRADUALLY GROW IN THE SHALLOW WATER – SEDIMENTARY ROCKS CONSISTING MAINLY OF COLONIES OF CYANOBACTERIA AND CALCIUM DEPOSITS. OXYGEN CONQUERS THE WORLD.

CAMBRIAN, 542-488 MILLION YEARS AGO: OXYGEN IS REQUIRED FOR ANIMALS TO DEVELOP. ALMOST ALL GROUPS OF ANIMALS HAVE THEIR ORIGINS HERE.

SILURIAN, 444-416 MILLION YEARS AGO: THE FIRST PIONEERS ON LAND DEFY THE DANGEROUS UV RADIATION.

* NAMES AND TERMS MARKED WITH AN *ASTERISK ARE EXPLAINED IN THE GLOSSARY.

DEVONIAN, 416-359 MILLION YEARS AGO: AFTER ARTHROPODS, MOLLUSCS AND PLANTS, FISH MOVE ONTO THE LAND.

CARBONIFEROUS, 359-299 MILLION YEARS AGO: THE EARTH IS COVERED BY FORESTS OF LYCOPSIDS UP TO 40 METRES HIGH.

SINCE THIS TIME, HEAT AND PRESSURE HAVE BEEN TURNING DEAD FORESTS INTO COAL. THE *CARBON BOUND IN THE PLANTS IS STORED IN THE GROUND.

PEAT AND WOOD

PLANTS THAT HAVE SUNK IN THE SWAMP TURN INTO PEAT IN THE ABSENCE OF AIR.

SANDS AND CLAYS

LIGNITE

WHEN THE SEA FLOODS THE SWAMP, SEDIMENTS COVER THESE LAYERS OF PEAT.

PEAT AND WOOD

LIGNITE

AS THE PRESSURE BUILDS UP AND THE TEMPERATURE RISES, LIGNITE IS FORMED FIRST.

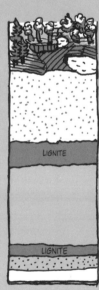

LIGNITE

LIGNITE

THE MORE LAYERS ARE DEPOSITED, THE MORE WATER IS FORCED OUT OF THE LIGNITE.

COAL

COAL

THE LIGNITE GRADUALLY BECOMES COAL, WHICH WE ARE STILL MINING TODAY.

PARALLEL TO THIS, CRUDE OIL AND NATURAL GAS FORM ON THE SEABED FROM DEAD MARINE ORGANISMS SUCH AS PLANKTON AND ALGAE IN THE ABSENCE OF OXYGEN.

MICROSCOPIC ORGANISMS SINK TO THE BOTTOM.

SEDIMENTS ARE DEPOSITED. ANAEROBIC BACTERIA TRANSFORM THE REMAINS OF THE MICROORGANISMS INTO BITUMEN, A PRECURSOR OF CRUDE OIL.

CRUDE OIL AND NATURAL GAS FINALLY FORM UNDER HIGH PRESSURE AND AT HIGH TEMPERATURES; THEY COLLECT IN SO-CALLED RESERVOIR ROCKS.

JURASSIC, 200-145 MILLION YEARS AGO: ANIMALS AND PLANTS HAVE DEVELOPED IN EVER GREATER DIVERSITY – INCLUDING DINOSAURS AS TALL AS A HOUSE.

CRETACEOUS, 145-65 MILLION YEARS AGO: EMERGENCE OF FLOWERING PLANTS.

TERTIARY, 65-2.6 MILLION YEARS AGO: AT THE TRANSITION BETWEEN THE CRETACEOUS AND THE TERTIARY, ABOUT HALF OF ALL ANIMAL SPECIES ON EARTH DIE OUT.

8

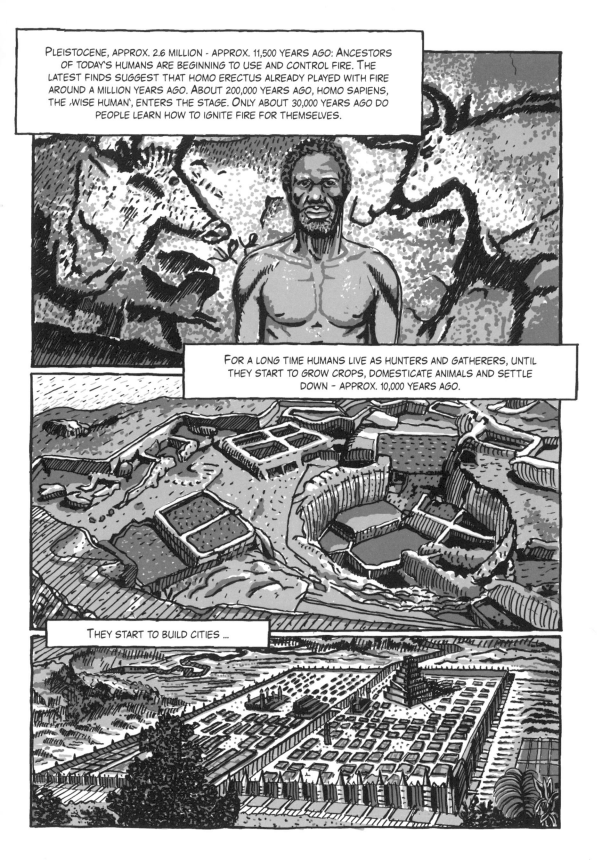

PLEISTOCENE, APPROX. 2.6 MILLION - APPROX. 11,500 YEARS AGO: ANCESTORS OF TODAY'S HUMANS ARE BEGINNING TO USE AND CONTROL FIRE. THE LATEST FINDS SUGGEST THAT HOMO ERECTUS ALREADY PLAYED WITH FIRE AROUND A MILLION YEARS AGO. ABOUT 200,000 YEARS AGO, HOMO SAPIENS, THE ‚WISE HUMAN', ENTERS THE STAGE. ONLY ABOUT 30,000 YEARS AGO DO PEOPLE LEARN HOW TO IGNITE FIRE FOR THEMSELVES.

FOR A LONG TIME HUMANS LIVE AS HUNTERS AND GATHERERS, UNTIL THEY START TO GROW CROPS, DOMESTICATE ANIMALS AND SETTLE DOWN – APPROX. 10,000 YEARS AGO.

THEY START TO BUILD CITIES ...

... AND REPLACE MUSCLE POWER WITH MACHINES.

THE AGE OF INDUSTRIALIZATION BEGINS IN THE MID-18TH CENTURY.

WITH IT, THE DEMAND FOR ENERGY RISES.

TO GENERATE ENERGY, HUMANS BURN THE FOSSIL CARBON STORED IN COAL, CRUDE OIL AND GAS CONVERTING IT TO CO_2 WITH THE AID OF OXYGEN.

THE LIBERATED CO_2 IS ADDED TO THE NATURAL CO_2 IN THE ATMOSPHERE, THUS CAUSING THE HUMAN-MADE GREENHOUSE EFFECT: THE GLOBAL CLIMATE STARTS TO WARM UP.

CHAPTER 1

WHY WE NEED TO TRANSFORM OURSELVES

HANS JOACHIM (JOHN) SCHELLNHUBER IS DIRECTOR OF THE POTSDAM INSTITUTE FOR CLIMATE IMPACT RESEARCH (PIK). HE IS ALSO EXTERNAL PROFESSOR AT THE *SANTA FE INSTITUTE, CHAIRMAN OF THE *CLIMATE KIC AND CHAIR OF THE GERMAN ADVISORY COUNCIL ON GLOBAL CHANGE (WBGU).

POTSDAM, TELEGRAFENBERG, ALBERT EINSTEIN SCIENCE PARK

SINCE THE BEGINNING OF INDUSTRIALIZATION THE SCALE OF MAN-MADE ENVIRONMENTAL CHANGES HAS REACHED A NEW DIMENSION.

AT THAT TIME ABOUT ONE BILLION PEOPLE LIVED ON EARTH. TODAY THERE ARE 7 BILLION OF US, AND IN 2050 ABOUT 9 BILLION PEOPLE WILL INHABIT THIS PLANET.

ON THE WAY TO HIS OFFICE, JOHN PASSES THE FAMOUS EINSTEIN TOWER.

MANY AREAS OF OUR NATURAL ENVIRONMENT REVEAL CRITICAL DEVELOPMENTS.

SOIL, FRESH WATER RESOURCES, FORESTS AND OCEANS ARE BEING OVER-EXPLOITED OR EVEN DESTROYED.

BIODIVERSITY, THE RICHNESS OF NATURE, IS DECLINING DRAMATICALLY.

CO_2

AND THE HUMAN INFLUENCE ON BASIC CHEMICAL PROCESSES LIKE FOR INSTANCE THE *CARBON CYCLE IS ENORMOUS.

15

WHAT IS AT STAKE IS THE ABILITY OF THE EARTH SYSTEM TO CONTINUE PROVIDING HUMAN CIVILIZATION WITH THE STABLE LIFE-SUPPORT SYSTEM IN WHICH WE EVOLVED.

IF WE DO NOT TURN DOWN THE HEAT WE SHALL COLLIDE WITH THE *PLANETARY GUARD RAILS.

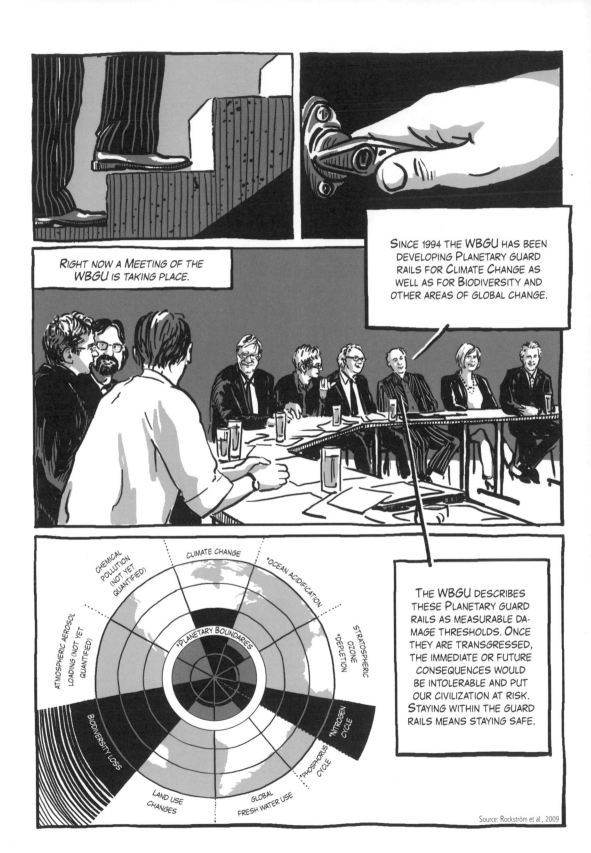

RIGHT NOW A MEETING OF THE WBGU IS TAKING PLACE.

SINCE 1994 THE WBGU HAS BEEN DEVELOPING PLANETARY GUARD RAILS FOR CLIMATE CHANGE AS WELL AS FOR BIODIVERSITY AND OTHER AREAS OF GLOBAL CHANGE.

THE WBGU DESCRIBES THESE PLANETARY GUARD RAILS AS MEASURABLE DAMAGE THRESHOLDS. ONCE THEY ARE TRANSGRESSED, THE IMMEDIATE OR FUTURE CONSEQUENCES WOULD BE INTOLERABLE AND PUT OUR CIVILIZATION AT RISK. STAYING WITHIN THE GUARD RAILS MEANS STAYING SAFE.

CHEMICAL POLLUTION (NOT YET QUANTIFIED)

CLIMATE CHANGE

*OCEAN ACIDIFICATION

ATMOSPHERIC AEROSOL LOADING (NOT YET QUANTIFIED)

*PLANETARY BOUNDARIES

STRATOSPHERIC OZONE *DEPLETION

BIODIVERSITY LOSS

*NITROGEN CYCLE

*PHOSPHORUS CYCLE

LAND USE CHANGES

GLOBAL FRESH WATER USE

Source: Rockström et al., 2009

SINCE THERE SHOULD BE SOMEONE SPEAKING FOR FUTURE GENERATIONS, I HAVE REPEATEDLY SUGGESTED APPOINTING OMBUDSPEOPLE TO REPRESENT THOSE WHO DO NOT YET HAVE A VOTE IN PARLIAMENT. THIS WOULD BE AN EXTENSION OF DEMOCRACY.

THE PAST SHOWS THAT PEOPLE AND ENTIRE CIVILIZATIONS HAVE THE ABILITY TO CHANGE. FOR INSTANCE, AROUND 11,000 YEARS AGO PEOPLE STARTED TO PURSUE ...

... AGRICULTURE AND STOCK FARMING. THEY CHANGED FROM A NOMADIC TO A SEDENTARY SOCIETY. THIS ALSO BECAME POSSIBLE BECAUSE THE CLIMATE HAD STABILIZED AND GROWN INTO A RELIABLE FACTOR.

STONE AGE

NEOLITHIC AGE
11 000 YEARS AGO

CHAPTER 2

PLANET EARTH IN THE ANTHROPOCENE – THE AGE OF HUMANS

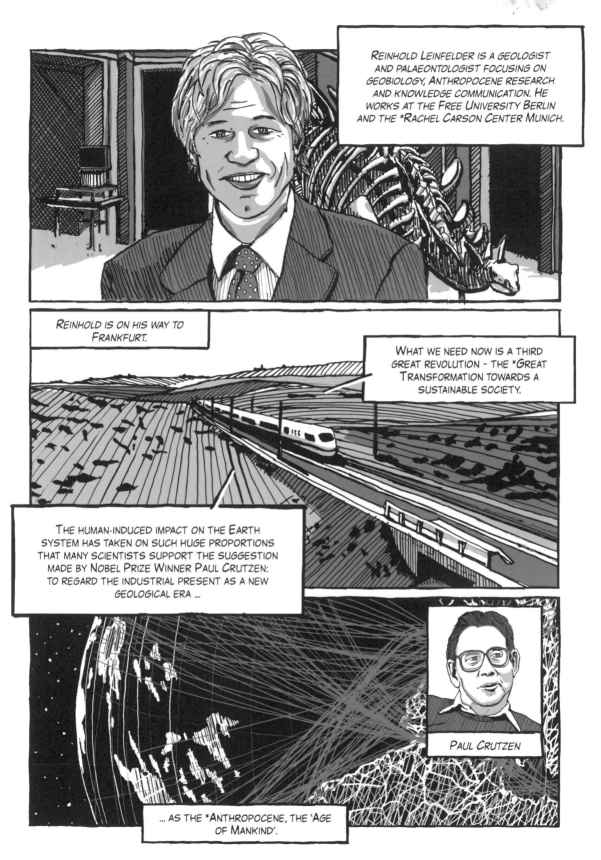

REINHOLD LEINFELDER IS A GEOLOGIST AND PALAEONTOLOGIST FOCUSING ON GEOBIOLOGY, ANTHROPOCENE RESEARCH AND KNOWLEDGE COMMUNICATION. HE WORKS AT THE FREE UNIVERSITY BERLIN AND THE *RACHEL CARSON CENTER MUNICH.

REINHOLD IS ON HIS WAY TO FRANKFURT.

WHAT WE NEED NOW IS A THIRD GREAT REVOLUTION – THE *GREAT TRANSFORMATION TOWARDS A SUSTAINABLE SOCIETY.

THE HUMAN-INDUCED IMPACT ON THE EARTH SYSTEM HAS TAKEN ON SUCH HUGE PROPORTIONS THAT MANY SCIENTISTS SUPPORT THE SUGGESTION MADE BY NOBEL PRIZE WINNER PAUL CRUTZEN: TO REGARD THE INDUSTRIAL PRESENT AS A NEW GEOLOGICAL ERA ...

PAUL CRUTZEN

... AS THE *ANTHROPOCENE, THE 'AGE OF MANKIND'.

FOR MILLENNIA, HUMANS HAVE REBELLED AGAINST THE SUPERPOWER WE CALL 'NATURE'.

IN THE 19TH AND 20TH CENTURIES, NEW TECHNOLOGIES, FOSSIL FUELS AND A FAST-GROWING POPULATION LED TO HUGE CHANGES IN THE EARTH SYSTEM.

WE TOOK CONTROL OF NATURE – INCLUDING THE CLIMATE, THE ENVIRONMENT, EVEN DNA.

OVER-RIPE FRUIT

'ANTI-MUSH GENE'

LONG-LASTING FRUIT

TODAY, WE NO LONGER LIVE IN 'BIOMES', I.E. NATURAL HABITATS, ...

... BUT IN 'ANTHROMES': HUMAN-MADE CULTURAL LANDSCAPES.

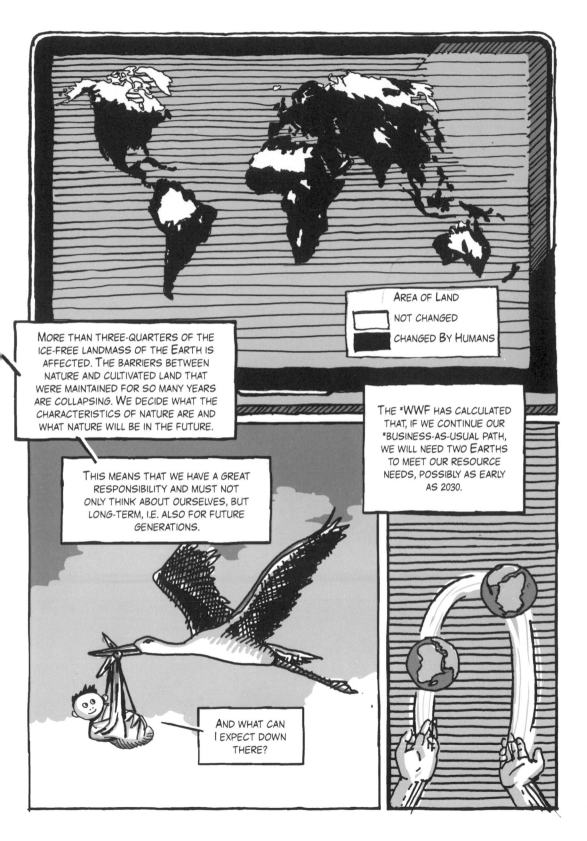

THE EXPANSION OF AREAS UNDER CULTIVATION BY DEFORESTATION AND OVERGRAZING IS LEADING TO SOIL DEGRADATION. WE LOSE UP TO 24 MILLION TONNES OF SURFACE SOIL EVERY YEAR AS A RESULT OF EROSION – THE SOIL OF AN AREA THE SIZE OF SWITZERLAND. AND THIS IS IRREVERSIBLE.

*SALINIZATION AND *DESERTIFICATION ARE FURTHER CONSEQUENCES OF OVERUSE. THE PROBLEM HAS BECOME ESPECIALLY EVIDENT IN CHINA. SEVERAL TIMES A YEAR, WHEN STORMS BLOW DESERT SAND INTO BEIJING FROM THE NORTH, THE ALARM IS SOUNDED IN THE CITY BECAUSE OF THE RISK OF RESPIRATORY PROBLEMS.

THE DEVASTATION OF SUCH LARGE TRACTS OF LAND THERE HAD TAKEN ON SUCH PROPORTIONS THAT THE GOVERNMENT LAUNCHED A GIGANTIC REAFFORESTATION PROGRAMME IN 1970.

A BELT OF FOREST ALMOST 4,500 KM LONG IS BEING PLANTED IN A TOTAL OF 13 PROVINCES. 35 MILLION HECTARES OF FOREST ARE TO BE PLANTED OVER A PERIOD OF ALMOST 80 YEARS. THAT'S AN AREA ABOUT THE SIZE OF GERMANY.

WE'RE GRADUALLY BEGINNING TO REALIZE THAT MANY OF THE RAW MATERIALS WE USE ARE FINITE. ORES, CRUDE OIL AND NATURAL GAS ARE THE BEST KNOWN EXAMPLES. AS LATE AS 2004 IT WAS BELIEVED THE EXTRACTION OF CRUDE OIL WOULD PEAK IN 2007. ALTHOUGH NEW RESOURCES ARE BEING TAPPED ALL THE TIME BY NEW TECHNOLOGIES, E.G. *FRACKING, THEY ALL TEND TO INVOLVE IMMENSE ENVIRONMENTAL DAMAGE.

CONVENTIONAL CRUDE OIL AND NATURAL GAS PRODUCTION IN BILLIONS OF BARRELS

NATURAL GAS DEPOSITS
ARCTIC/ANTARCTIC
DEEP SEA
HEAVY OIL
MIDDLE EAST
OTHERS
RUSSIA
EUROPE
*US 48

Source: ASPO 2004

WE NEED LITHIUM FOR BATTERIES AND *RARE EARTHS AND METALS FOR INDUSTRIAL PRODUCTION.

WE EXTRACT THEM FROM CONCENTRATED DEPOSITS ...

... AND SPREAD THEM ALL OVER THE WORLD WHEN WE DISPOSE OF ELECTRONIC WASTE AND EXCAVATED MATERIAL.

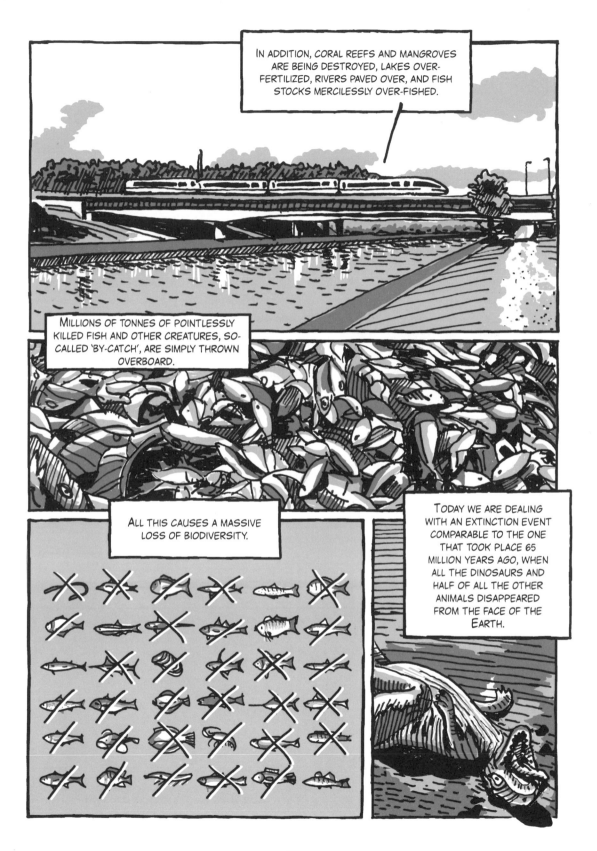

FRANKFURT → PANAMA

WE WILL ALSO HAVE TO DEAL WITH THE ISSUE OF WATER IN A DIFFERENT FORM, BECAUSE IT'S NOT ONLY GETTING SCARCER, IT'S ALSO BEING POLLUTED BY INDUSTRY, AGRICULTURE AND HOUSEHOLDS.

LITTLE OR NO WATER SCARCITY

LOOMING PHYSICAL WATER SCARCITY

PHYSICAL WATER SCARCITY

ECONOMIC WATER SCARCITY

NO DATA AVAILABLE

A THIRD OF HUMANITY IS AFFECTED BY *WATER SCARCITY, AND ABOUT 800 MILLION PEOPLE HAVE NO ACCESS TO SAFE DRINKING WATER ...

Source: UNESCO 2009

... WHILE OTHERS HAVE MORE THAN ENOUGH TO BATHE IN.

HOW DEATH ZONES ARE FORMED

HEAT

FRESH WATER

SALT WATER

OXYGEN

LIVING ORGANISMS

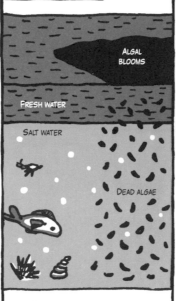

ALGAL BLOOMS

FRESH WATER

SALT WATER

DEAD ALGAE

DYING FISH

FRESH WATER

LOW-OXYGEN SALT WATER

DEATH ZONE

Source: The Times Picayune 2007

THE WARMING OF THE OCEAN MAKES THE LAYERS OF WATER MORE STABLE; THIS PREVENTS OXYGEN FROM THE AIR PENETRATING TO DEEPER REGIONS OF THE SEA. WARM, FRESH WATER FROM RIVER ESTUARIES REINFORCES THIS EFFECT.

NITROGEN AND PHOSPHORUS FROM FERTILIZERS AND SEWAGE CAUSE ALGAE TO GROW QUICKLY. DEAD ALGAE SINK AND DECOMPOSE. AS A RESULT, OXYGEN IS ALSO CONSUMED IN DEEPER LAYERS.

THE OXYGEN IS COMPLETELY USED UP – DEATH ZONES FORM WHERE FISH AND MICRO-ORGANISMS DIE EN MASSE.

DEATH ZONES IN EUROPE

NITROGEN FERTILIZERS AND PHOSPHATES – ESSENTIAL FOR FOOD PRODUCTION – ARE PUTTING IMMENSE STRAIN ON OUR ECOSYSTEMS. ALMOST HALF OF THEM END UP IN THE OCEAN, AND THERE THEY LEAD TO THE CREATION OF LOW-OXYGEN DEATH ZONES, WHICH ARE UNINHABITABLE FOR MOST ORGANISMS. ONE OF THE BIGGEST UNDERWATER DESERTS IS IN THE BALTIC SEA.

GLOBAL ENVIRONMENTAL CHANGES CAN MUTUALLY REINFORCE OR WEAKEN EACH OTHER. BUT THE MOST COMMON EFFECT IS MUTUAL REINFORCEMENT. IT TRIGGERS ABRUPT, NON-LINEAR CHANGES IN ESSENTIAL CHARACTERISTICS OF THE EARTH SYSTEM.

Source: Nasa / Earth Observatory 2008

BOCAS DEL TORO, PANAMA

34

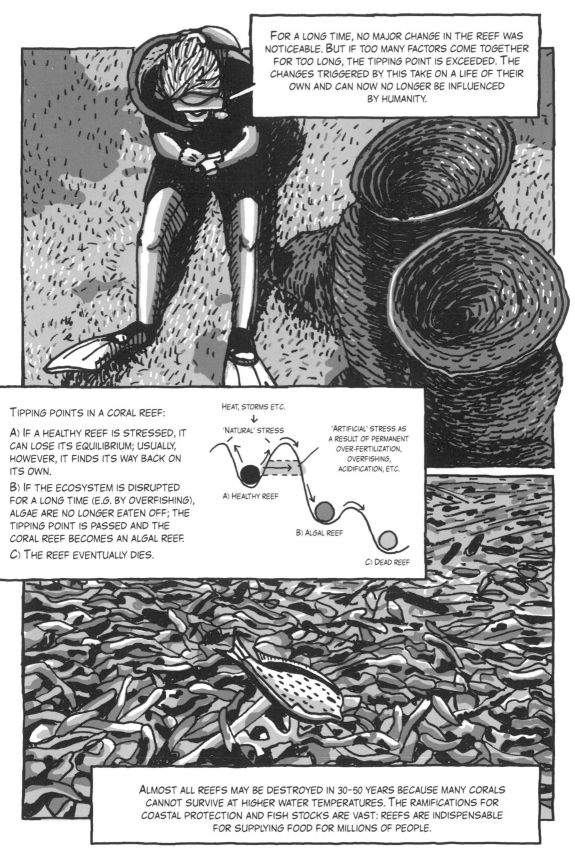

FOR A LONG TIME, NO MAJOR CHANGE IN THE REEF WAS NOTICEABLE. BUT IF TOO MANY FACTORS COME TOGETHER FOR TOO LONG, THE TIPPING POINT IS EXCEEDED. THE CHANGES TRIGGERED BY THIS TAKE ON A LIFE OF THEIR OWN AND CAN NOW NO LONGER BE INFLUENCED BY HUMANITY.

TIPPING POINTS IN A CORAL REEF:

A) IF A HEALTHY REEF IS STRESSED, IT CAN LOSE ITS EQUILIBRIUM; USUALLY, HOWEVER, IT FINDS ITS WAY BACK ON ITS OWN.

B) IF THE ECOSYSTEM IS DISRUPTED FOR A LONG TIME (E.G. BY OVERFISHING), ALGAE ARE NO LONGER EATEN OFF; THE TIPPING POINT IS PASSED AND THE CORAL REEF BECOMES AN ALGAL REEF.

C) THE REEF EVENTUALLY DIES.

HEAT, STORMS ETC.

'NATURAL' STRESS

'ARTIFICIAL' STRESS AS A RESULT OF PERMANENT OVER-FERTILIZATION, OVERFISHING, ACIDIFICATION, ETC.

A) HEALTHY REEF

B) ALGAL REEF

C) DEAD REEF

ALMOST ALL REEFS MAY BE DESTROYED IN 30–50 YEARS BECAUSE MANY CORALS CANNOT SURVIVE AT HIGHER WATER TEMPERATURES. THE RAMIFICATIONS FOR COASTAL PROTECTION AND FISH STOCKS ARE VAST: REEFS ARE INDISPENSABLE FOR SUPPLYING FOOD FOR MILLIONS OF PEOPLE.

CHAPTER 3
HOT STUFF: CLIMATE CHANGE

STEFAN RAHMSTORF IS PROFESSOR OF PHYSICS OF THE OCEANS AT POTSDAM UNIVERSITY AND HEAD OF EARTH SYSTEM ANALYSIS AT THE POTSDAM INSTITUTE FOR CLIMATE IMPACT RESEARCH. HIS RESEARCH FOCUSES ON THE ROLE OF THE OCEANS IN CLIMATE CHANGE.

THE RESEARCH SHIP STANLEY R. RIGGS IS IN ROANOKE SOUND BY THE OUTER BANKS NEAR NAG'S HEAD, NORTH CAROLINA, USA.

NAG'S HEAD

PACIFIC

NORTH CAROLINA

ATLANTIC

HUMANITY IS RESPONSIBLE FOR THE GLOBAL TEMPERATURE RISE WE ARE EXPERIENCING TODAY. FIRSTLY AS A RESULT OF THE USE OF FOSSIL FUELS; SECONDLY AS A RESULT OF DEFORESTATION.

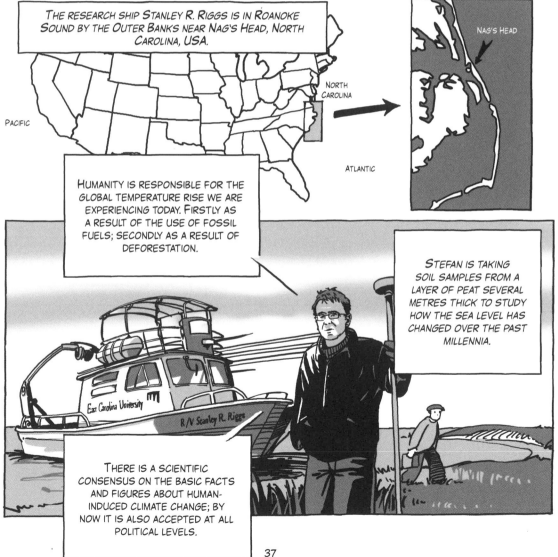

STEFAN IS TAKING SOIL SAMPLES FROM A LAYER OF PEAT SEVERAL METRES THICK TO STUDY HOW THE SEA LEVEL HAS CHANGED OVER THE PAST MILLENNIA.

East Carolina University

R/V Stanley R. Riggs

THERE IS A SCIENTIFIC CONSENSUS ON THE BASIC FACTS AND FIGURES ABOUT HUMAN-INDUCED CLIMATE CHANGE; BY NOW IT IS ALSO ACCEPTED AT ALL POLITICAL LEVELS.

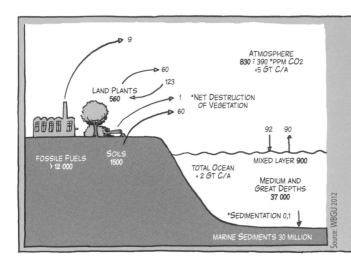

CARBON (C) FLOWS IN GIGATONNES (GT) PER ANNUM
(BOLD TYPE: TOTAL AMOUNTS OF STORED CARBON IN GT)

WHEN THERE IS NO HUMAN INTERFERENCE, THE *CARBON CYCLE IS IN EQUILIBRIUM. HOWEVER, OUR USE OF FOSSIL FUELS IS INCREASING THE AMOUNT OF ATMOSPHERIC CARBON BY 5 GIGATONNES A YEAR.

THE CONCENTRATION OF CO_2 IN THE ATMOSPHERE HAS INCREASED RAPIDLY SINCE CA. 1850, FROM 280 PPM (A TYPICAL VALUE FOR WARM INTERGLACIAL PERIODS) TO OVER 390 PPM. CO_2 IS A RADIATIVE FORCING GAS: THE HIGHER ITS CONCENTRATION IN THE ATMOSPHERE, THE MORE THE SURFACE TEMPERATURES RISE. IF THE CO_2 CONTENT IN THE AIR DOUBLES, THE AVERAGE GLOBAL TEMPERATURE RISES BY 2-4°C.

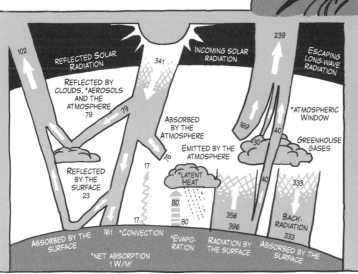

SUNLIGHT SHINES ON THE EARTH.

A THIRD OF IT IS REFLECTED, THE REST IS CONVERTED INTO HEAT IN THE ATMOSPHERE AND ON THE EARTH'S SURFACE.

THE EARTH CAN ONLY GET RID OF HEAT BY RADIATING IT BACK OUT INTO SPACE.

HOWEVER, GREENHOUSE GASES PREVENT THE ATMOSPHERE FROM LETTING LONG-WAVE THERMAL RADIATION THROUGH. A LOT OF THE RADIATION EMITTED FROM THE SURFACE IS ABSORBED AND RERADIATED BACK DOWN.

GLOBAL ENERGY FLOWS AND GREENHOUSE-GAS EFFECT, DATA IN WATTS/M²

Data: IPCC 2007

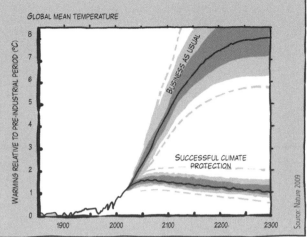

GLOBAL MEAN TEMPERATURE

BUSINESS AS USUAL

SUCCESSFUL CLIMATE PROTECTION

WARMING RELATIVE TO PRE-INDUSTRIAL PERIOD (°C)

1900 2000 2100 2200 2300

Source: Nature 2009

IF WE DO NOT CHANGE OUR WAYS SOON, WE EXPECT TEMPERATURES TO INCREASE BY AN AVERAGE OF 4-7°C OVER THE NEXT 100 YEARS.

BY TAKING RESOLUTE MEASURES TO PROTECT THE CLIMATE, WE COULD LIMIT WARMING TO 2°C, BUT ONLY IF WE START TAKING ACTION STRAIGHT AWAY.

ICE-COVERED REGIONS DURING THE PLEISTOCENE

BY WAY OF COMPARISON, THE LAST GREAT GLOBAL WARMING TOOK PLACE AT THE END OF THE LAST ICE AGE APPROXIMATELY 15,000 YEARS AGO. OVER A PERIOD OF 5,000 YEARS THE GLOBAL TEMPERATURE ROSE BY APPROXIMATELY 5°C. AN UNLIMITED MAN-MADE GLOBAL WARMING COULD REACH SUCH A SCALE IN A FRACTION OF THAT TIME – AND IT'S STARTING FROM A CLIMATE THAT'S ALREADY WARM.

THE EXACT COORDINATES AND ELEVATION OF THE SITE ARE DETERMINED USING GPS AND LASERS.

THE EVIDENCE FOR THE IMPACT OF OUR GREENHOUSE-GAS EMISSIONS ON THE CLIMATE IS BASED ON DECADES OF RESEARCH WORK AND THOUSANDS OF STUDIES. IT'S PRACTICALLY INCONCEIVABLE THAT THIS COULD ALL BE SUDDENLY OVERTURNED BY NEW RESULTS.

THE GLOBAL TEMPERATURE IS RELATIVELY EASY TO PREDICT, BUT IT'S MUCH MORE DIFFICULT TO PREDICT THE EFFECTS OF WARMING ON THE ICE MASSES, THE SEA LEVEL OR VEGETATION.

REGIONAL DIFFERENCES IN WARMING, ASSUMING A MEAN GLOBAL WARMING OF ABOUT 4°C UP UNTIL THE END OF THE CENTURY. THE CONTINENTS AND POLAR REGIONS ARE THE MOST SERIOUSLY AFFECTED.

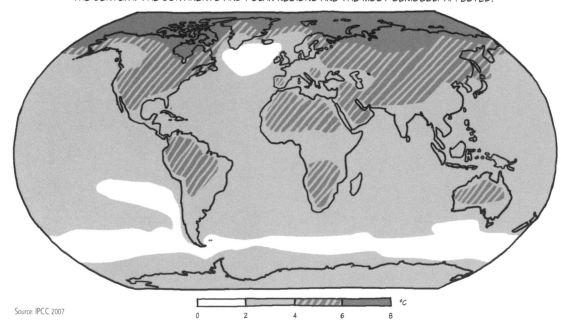

Source: IPCC 2007

°C
0   2   4   6   8

STEFAN COMES ON BOARD TO TAKE SEDIMENT CORES IN THE LAGOON.

AND THE *TIPPING ELEMENTS MAKE LIFE EVEN MORE DIFFICULT FOR US: CERTAIN REGIONS OR PROCESSES REACT PARTICULARLY SENSITIVELY AND ACT AS SELF-REINFORCING ELEMENTS IN THE SYSTEM. WHEN THE HIGHLY REFLECTIVE ICE SURFACES MELT, THIS REVEALS THE DARK OCEAN, WHICH ABSORBS MUCH MORE SOLAR HEAT AND FURTHER ACCELERATES THE MELTING.

JUST ONE EXAMPLE: HALF OF THE SUMMER SEA-ICE COVER ON THE ARCTIC OCEAN HAS ALREADY DISAPPEARED.

COMPARISON OF THE EXTENT OF THE ARCTIC SEA ICE IN 1979 AND 2012

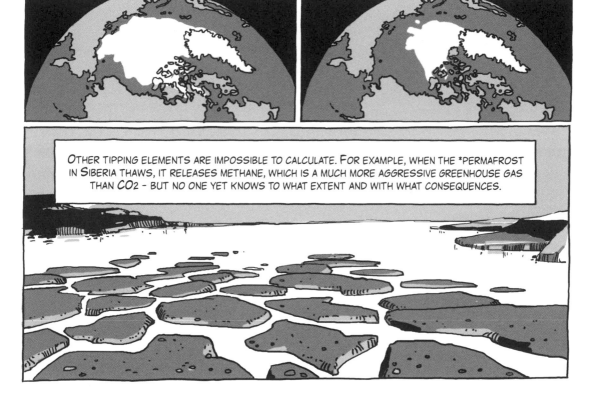

OTHER TIPPING ELEMENTS ARE IMPOSSIBLE TO CALCULATE. FOR EXAMPLE, WHEN THE *PERMAFROST IN SIBERIA THAWS, IT RELEASES METHANE, WHICH IS A MUCH MORE AGGRESSIVE GREENHOUSE GAS THAN CO_2 – BUT NO ONE YET KNOWS TO WHAT EXTENT AND WITH WHAT CONSEQUENCES.

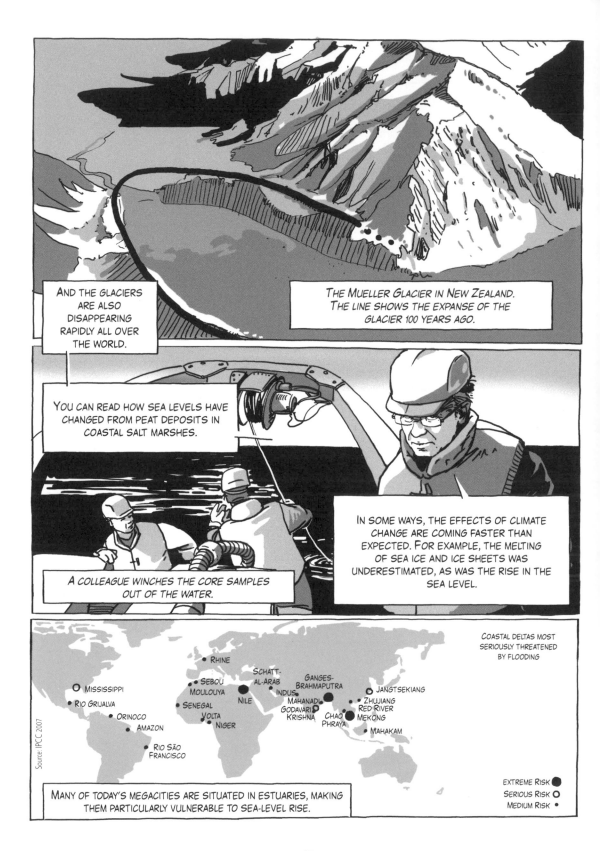

AND THE GLACIERS ARE ALSO DISAPPEARING RAPIDLY ALL OVER THE WORLD.

THE MUELLER GLACIER IN NEW ZEALAND. THE LINE SHOWS THE EXPANSE OF THE GLACIER 100 YEARS AGO.

YOU CAN READ HOW SEA LEVELS HAVE CHANGED FROM PEAT DEPOSITS IN COASTAL SALT MARSHES.

A COLLEAGUE WINCHES THE CORE SAMPLES OUT OF THE WATER.

IN SOME WAYS, THE EFFECTS OF CLIMATE CHANGE ARE COMING FASTER THAN EXPECTED. FOR EXAMPLE, THE MELTING OF SEA ICE AND ICE SHEETS WAS UNDERESTIMATED, AS WAS THE RISE IN THE SEA LEVEL.

COASTAL DELTAS MOST SERIOUSLY THREATENED BY FLOODING

RHINE

MISSISSIPPI

RIO GRIJALVA

ORINOCO

AMAZON

RIO SÃO FRANCISCO

SEBOU
MOULOUYA

SENEGAL

VOLTA

NIGER

SCHATT-AL-ARAB

NILE

INDUS

GANGES-BRAHMAPUTRA

MAHANADI
GODAVARI
KRISHNA

CHAO PHRAYA

JANGTSEKIANG

ZHUJIANG
RED RIVER
MEKONG

MAHAKAM

Source: IPCC 2007

MANY OF TODAY'S MEGACITIES ARE SITUATED IN ESTUARIES, MAKING THEM PARTICULARLY VULNERABLE TO SEA-LEVEL RISE.

EXTREME RISK ●
SERIOUS RISK ○
MEDIUM RISK ·

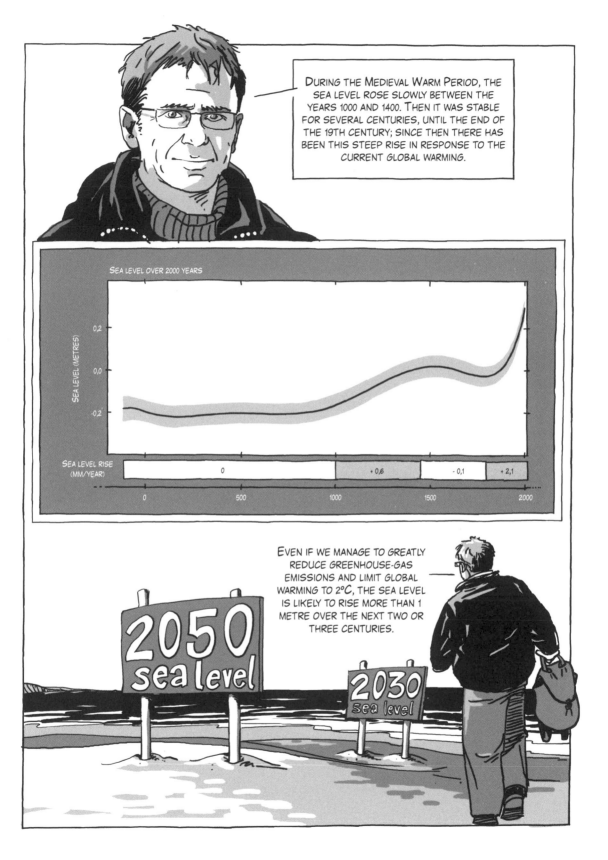

DURING THE MEDIEVAL WARM PERIOD, THE SEA LEVEL ROSE SLOWLY BETWEEN THE YEARS 1000 AND 1400. THEN IT WAS STABLE FOR SEVERAL CENTURIES, UNTIL THE END OF THE 19TH CENTURY; SINCE THEN THERE HAS BEEN THIS STEEP RISE IN RESPONSE TO THE CURRENT GLOBAL WARMING.

SEA LEVEL OVER 2000 YEARS

SEA LEVEL (METRES)

0,2

0,0

-0,2

SEA LEVEL RISE (MM/YEAR)

| 0 | + 0,6 | - 0,1 | + 2,1 |

0   500   1000   1500   2000

EVEN IF WE MANAGE TO GREATLY REDUCE GREENHOUSE-GAS EMISSIONS AND LIMIT GLOBAL WARMING TO 2°C, THE SEA LEVEL IS LIKELY TO RISE MORE THAN 1 METRE OVER THE NEXT TWO OR THREE CENTURIES.

2050 sea level

2030 sea level

THIS PUTS COASTAL CITIES AND LOW-LYING ISLANDS AT RISK. HURRICANES LIKE SANDY, WHICH HIT NEW YORK IN OCTOBER 2012 – CAUSING DEVASTATING DAMAGE, FLOODED ROADS AND SUBWAYS, POWER FAILURES AND MANY DEATHS – HIGHLIGHT THE URGENCY OF THE PROBLEM. BECAUSE COASTAL FLOODING FROM HURRICANES WILL GET WORSE AS THE SEA LEVEL RISES.

THE RISK OF EXTREME WEATHER EVENTS IS ALSO INCREASING. THE NUMBER OF FLOODS, DROUGHTS AND FOREST FIRES WILL INCREASE WORLDWIDE.

STEFAN ON HIS WAY TO A WORKSHOP ON COASTAL PROTECTION IN NAG'S HEAD.

AND OF COURSE, THIS HAS AN EFFECT ON THE WATER SUPPLY AND FOOD SECURITY. BOTH THE MODELS AND THE DATA SHOW AN INCREASE IN THE STRENGTH, AND POSSIBLY ALSO IN THE FREQUENCY, OF HURRICANES AS A RESULT OF HIGHER SEA SURFACE TEMPERATURES.

FOREST FIRES IN SPAIN 2012

FLOODING IN SOUTHERN RUSSIA 2012

EXTREME DROUGHT IN THE USA 2012

HURRICANE KATRINA IN THE USA IN 2005

THE WATER IS RISING!

NAG'S HEAD

ALTHOUGH GLOBAL AGRICULTURAL PRODUCTION DOES NOT NECESSARILY HAVE TO DECLINE IN WARMER CLIMATIC CONDITIONS, SOME HARVESTS WILL BE LOST IN POORER AND WARMER COUNTRIES AS A RESULT OF WATER SCARCITY AND WEATHER EXTREMES.

THE WATER SUPPLY IN LIMA IS HIGHLY DEPENDENT ON THE ANDEAN GLACIERS. WHILE THE POPULATION IS GROWING, THE GLACIERS ARE MELTING, AND NO ONE CAN STOP THEM.

IF THE MOUNTAIN GLACIERS DISAPPEAR, THIS WILL THREATEN WATER SUPPLIES TO MAJOR CITIES LIKE LIMA.

TODAY AT 9 AM, STAKEHOLDER WORKSHOP SEA-LEVEL

VENICE 2012

IT'S NOT EASY TO PREDICT THE EXACT CONSEQUENCES OF SUCH A DRASTIC CHANGE IN THE CLIMATE, SO SURPRISES ARE QUITE POSSIBLE.

AT PRESENT, THE SEA LEVELS ARE RISING AT A RATE OF ABOUT 3 CM PER DECADE. BUT IF GLOBAL WARMING CONTINUES, THIS RATE WILL SPEED UP, SIMPLY BECAUSE THE ICE MASSES MELT FASTER THE WARMER IT BECOMES. IT COULD REACH 10 CM PER DECADE. THAT WOULD MAKE IT A LOT MORE DIFFICULT FOR US HUMANS TO ADAPT TO SEA-LEVEL RISE.

*STAKEHOLDERS WORKSHOP, NAG'S HEAD 2012: STEFAN TALKS WITH REPRESENTATIVES OF THE PLANNING AND ENVIRONMENTAL AUTHORITIES AND OTHER GROUPS WHO ARE INTERESTED IN CLIMATE CHANGE AND COASTAL PROTECTION.

CO_2 ACCUMULATES IN THE ATMOSPHERE BECAUSE OF ITS LONG LIFESPAN, SO THAT FURTHER WARMING CAN ONLY BE PREVENTED IF WE GET OUR ENERGY FROM A DIFFERENT SOURCE.

CHAPTER 4

WE'RE NOT THAT STUPID.
A GLANCE INTO THE PAST

DIRK MESSNER IS DIRECTOR OF THE *GERMAN DEVELOPMENT INSTITUTE (DIE) IN BONN, CO-DIRECTOR OF THE *CENTRE FOR ADVANCED STUDIES ON GLOBAL COOPERATION RESEARCH, DUISBURG, AND DEPUTY CHAIR OF THE WBGU.

DIRK'S CHAUFFEUR DROPS HIM OFF AT THE INSTITUTE.

AND DON'T FORGET, THE NEW CAR IS BEING DELIVERED TODAY.

OH! HOPE IT'S NOT ONE OF THOSE ELECTRIC THINGS; I TOLD YOU BEFORE THERE'S NO WAY I'M GOING TO DRIVE ONE OF THOSE.

IN THE GLOBAL GOVERNANCE SCHOOL AT THE GERMAN DEVELOPMENT INSTITUTE, DIRK HAS BEEN TRAINING SCIENTISTS AND PRACTIONERS FROM EIGHT *EMERGING ECONOMIES SINCE 2007.

TO MAKE SURE THAT THE AMOUNTS OF CO_2 DON'T KEEP ON INCREASING, IT'S ESSENTIAL TO DECOUPLE GLOBAL ECONOMIC DEVELOPMENT FROM GREENHOUSE-GAS EMISSIONS, ESPECIALLY IN THE FIELDS OF ENERGY SUPPLY, URBANIZATION AND LAND USE.

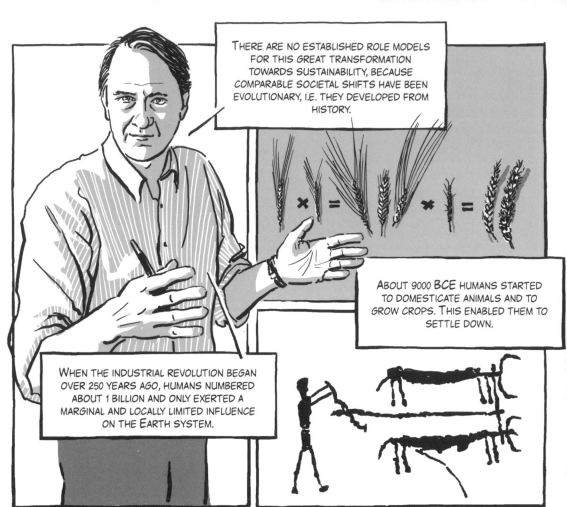

THERE ARE NO ESTABLISHED ROLE MODELS FOR THIS GREAT TRANSFORMATION TOWARDS SUSTAINABILITY, BECAUSE COMPARABLE SOCIETAL SHIFTS HAVE BEEN EVOLUTIONARY, I.E. THEY DEVELOPED FROM HISTORY.

ABOUT 9000 BCE HUMANS STARTED TO DOMESTICATE ANIMALS AND TO GROW CROPS. THIS ENABLED THEM TO SETTLE DOWN.

WHEN THE INDUSTRIAL REVOLUTION BEGAN OVER 250 YEARS AGO, HUMANS NUMBERED ABOUT 1 BILLION AND ONLY EXERTED A MARGINAL AND LOCALLY LIMITED INFLUENCE ON THE EARTH SYSTEM.

SLASH-AND-BURN FARMING IN FINLAND AROUND 1887. THE EFFECTS ON THE EARTH SYSTEM WERE STILL MANAGEABLE AT THAT TIME.

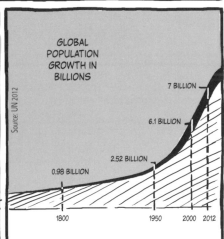

GLOBAL POPULATION GROWTH IN BILLIONS

Source: UN 2012

7 BILLION

6.1 BILLION

2.52 BILLION

0.98 BILLION

1800   1950   2000 2012

TODAY, HUMANS ARE THE BIGGEST GEOLOGICAL FORCE IN THE EARTH SYSTEM.

THE WORLD ECONOMY IS CHANGING RADICALLY. 1.3 BILLION PEOPLE BELONGED TO THE GLOBAL MIDDLE CLASS IN 1989, WITH 80% OF THEM LIVING IN THE INDUSTRIALIZED COUNTRIES. BY 2030 THE GLOBAL MIDDLE CLASS WILL NUMBER ABOUT 5 BILLION PEOPLE, AND 80% OF THEM WILL BE LIVING IN DEVELOPING COUNTRIES AND EMERGING ECONOMIES.

THE RECOVERY OF EMERGING ECONOMIES

DIFFERENT REGIONS' PERCENTAGE SHARES OF THE WORLD ECONOMY

REST OF THE WORLD

MIDDLE EAST

USA

JAPAN

RUSSIA

INDIA

WESTERN EUROPE

CHINA

1700   1820   1870   1900   1913   1950   1978   2003 2008   2015   2030   2050

FORECAST

Source: Die ZEIT 2008

IF THERE IS NO TRANSFORMATION TO SUSTAINABILITY, THIS DEVELOPMENT TREND WILL LEAD TO THE DEGRADATION OF THE NATURAL LIFE-SUPPORT SYSTEMS.

CHANGE OF VIEW

THE 'DISCOVERY' OF A LIFESTYLE THAT IS CONSCIOUSLY GEARED TOWARDS SUSTAINABILITY IS COMPARABLE TO THE ADVENT OF THE ENLIGHTENMENT IN THE 17TH CENTURY. BOTH CONCEPTS CALL FOR AN EXTENSIVE REORGANIZATION OF THE SOCIETY IN WHICH THEY EMERGED.

IMMANUEL KANT DESCRIBED THE ENLIGHTENMENT AS AN ESSENTIAL CHANGE IN THE WAY PEOPLE THINK, A NEW ERA FOR MANKIND IN WHICH THE NORMATIVE FOUNDATIONS OF HUMAN COEXISTENCE ARE REVOLUTIONIZED. THE PERSPECTIVE FROM WHICH PEOPLE JUDGED THEMSELVES AND THEIR SOCIETIES HAD FUNDAMENTALLY CHANGED.

ENLIGHTENMENT IS THE HUMAN BEING'S EMERGENCE FROM HIS SELF-INCURRED MINORITY.

A RELIGIOUS VIEW OF THE WORLD VERSUS A KNOWLEDGE-BASED VIEW OF THE WORLD

AS HUMANS WE MUST TAKE RESPONSIBILITY FOR THE STABILITY OF THE EARTH SYSTEM.

IS ALL THIS POSSIBLE?

SO THEREFORE, WE NEED TO COOPERATE GLOBALLY. WE NEED A GLOBAL SENSE OF COMMUNITY, A 'WE-IDENTITY'.

WE MUST INVENT A PRODUCTION AND CONSUMPTION MODEL FOR 9 BILLION PEOPLE – WITHIN THE LIMITS OF THE EARTH SYSTEM.

THE ENLIGHTENMENT WAS ABOUT THE INALIENABLE RIGHTS OF 'HUMAN RACE'; YET FOR MANY ENLIGHTENMENT THINKERS SLAVES WERE NOT PART OF IT.

DAVID HUME (1711-1776)

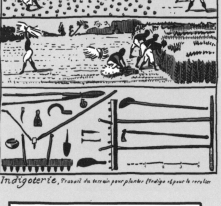

Indigoterie, Travail du terrain pour planter l'indigo et pour le recolter

DENIS DIDEROT (1713-1784)

MONTESQUIEU (1689-1755)

VOLTAIRE (1694-1778)

MANY PROPONENTS OF THE ENLIGHTENMENT WERE FANTASTIC FUTURE-ORIENTED MINDS AND VISIONARIES, BUT THEY WERE ALSO CHILDREN OF THEIR TIME. SLAVERY IS AN EXAMPLE OF THIS CONTRADICTION.

JEAN-JACQUES ROUSSEAU (1712-1778)

IMMANUEL KANT (1724-1804)

THE US CONSTITUTION OF 1787 BEGINS WITH THE FAMOUS FORMULA 'WE THE PEOPLE' – YET SLAVERY REMAINED PART OF SOCIETAL REALITY IN THE USA FOR ANOTHER EIGHT DECADES ...

... AND ULTIMATELY LED TO THE AMERICAN CIVIL WAR OF 1861-1865.

RIO DE JANEIRO, JUNE 2012

SO IT'S A LONG, HARD ROAD WITH MANY SETBACKS FROM A SOPHISTICATED PHILOSOPHY AND IDEA TO SOCIETAL REALITY. LINEAR PROGRESS IS UNKNOWN IN WORLD HISTORY.

SEEN FROM THIS PERSPECTIVE, THE SUSTAINABILITY PARADIGM HAS HAD A BREATHTAKING CAREER. EVEN THOUGH THE *UN CONFERENCE ON SUSTAINABLE DEVELOPMENT IN RIO MUST BE REGARDED AS A FAILURE.

RIO +20

United Nations Conference on Sustainable Development

RIO -20

NOTHING IS LEFT OF THE SPIRIT OF CHANGE AT THE FIRST *EARTH SUMMIT OF 1992. THE FINAL DECLARATION DID NOT GENERATE FRESH IMPETUS, AND THE LARGE NUMBER OF PROBLEMS ADDRESSED HAD THE EFFECT THAT NOT A SINGLE ONE WAS RESOLUTELY TACKLED. YOU COULD REALLY SPEAK OF A RIO MINUS 20 CONFERENCE.

However, scientists, the private sector and civil society are more advanced and more mature than political leaders in Washington, Brussels, Berlin, New Delhi and Beijing.

If the German *Energiewende succeeds, it could encourage emulators worldwide.

This was shown by the conference programme in Rio. The transformation towards sustainability is not a future project: it's already in full swing.

Peter Altmaier, German Federal Minister for the Environment

Rajendra Kumar Pachauri, Chair of the *Intergovernmental Panel on Climate Change (IPCC)

Jennifer Morgan, Director of the Climate and Energy Programme at the *World Resources Institute

Wind farm at Lake Turkana in Kenya

For example, in Rio de Janeiro over 50 developing countries in concert with many private companies committed themselves to ambitious initiatives for more sustainability in the energy sector. These included countries like Ghana, Bangladesh, India and Morocco.

55

A GROUP OF AFRICAN GOVERNMENTS, THE WORLD BANK, MAJOR PRIVATE FOUNDATIONS LIKE CONSERVATION INTERNATIONAL AND CORPORATIONS IN TURN AGREED CONCRETE INITIATIVES TO PROTECT NATURAL ASSETS IN AFRICAN COUNTRIES. PROJECTS LIKE THE CROSS-BORDER *PEACE PARKS FOCUS ON ENVIRONMENTAL PROTECTION AND ECOTOURISM. THESE APPROACHES WERE FURTHER DEVELOPED IN RIO.

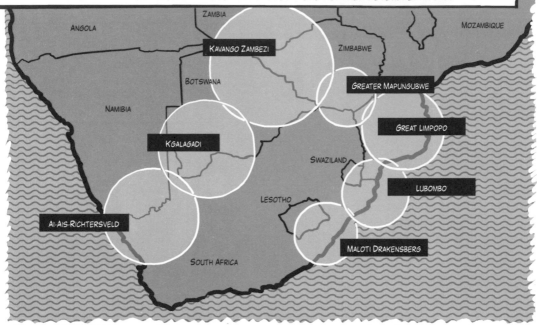

ANGOLA

ZAMBIA

MOZAMBIQUE

KAVANGO ZAMBEZI

ZIMBABWE

BOTSWANA

GREATER MAPUNGUBWE

NAMIBIA

GREAT LIMPOPO

KGALAGADI

SWAZILAND

LUBOMBO

LESOTHO

AI-AIS-RICHTERSVELD

MALOTI DRAKENSBERG

SOUTH AFRICA

Source: www.tfpd.co.za

SOLAR ENERGY PLANT NEAR MOUNT ABU IN RAJASTHAN, INDIA

CITIES FORGED ALLIANCES, AND CORPORATIONS PRESENTED THE LATEST ENVIRONMENTAL TECHNOLOGIES.

KANDEH K. YUMKELLA, DIRECTOR GENERAL OF THE UNITED NATIONS INDUSTRIAL DEVELOPMENT ORGANIZATION (UNIDO)

DIRK MEETS PAN JIAHUA, CHINESE CLIMATE SCIENTIST AND THE MOST HIGHLY RANKING CONSULTANT IN THE FIELD OF CLIMATE PROTECTION.

CURRENTLY THE TRANSFORMATION PROCESS MIGHT BE REACHING A TIPPING POINT.

ON THE ONE HAND, THE CURRENT GROWTH MODEL IS HISTORICALLY LEGITIMIZED, AND IT SEEMS TO BE RESISTANT TO CHANGE BECAUSE IT HAS LED TO ENORMOUS PROSPERITY IN MANY COUNTRIES.

ON THE OTHER HAND, THERE IS A BROAD CONSENSUS THAT THIS RESOURCE-WASTING AND CLIMATE-DAMAGING PATH OF DEVELOPMENT NO LONGER OFFERS A FUTURE FOR THE NEXT GENERATION. AND BECAUSE HARDLY ANYONE STILL BELIEVES IN THE FUTURE VIABILITY OF THE FOSSIL-BASED SOCIETY, PROSPECTS FOR REFORMS ARE EMERGING.

IN ADDITION, WE HAVE THE TECHNOLOGIES AND THE KNOWLEDGE FOR DESIGNING THE TRANSFORMATION.

IF CHINA AND EUROPE RESOLUTELY PURSUED A LOW-CARBON SOCIETY, THIS WOULD REPRESENT A BREAKTHROUGH AND OTHER COUNTRIES WOULD FOLLOW SUIT.

MANY THINGS HAVE STARTED MOVING. BUT THE TRANSFORMATION TO A LOW-CARBON SOCIETY CAN ALSO BE FOILED BY THE SO-CALLED REBOUND EFFECT. FOR EXAMPLE, CARS ARE BECOMING MORE AND MORE ENERGY EFFICIENT, AND CO_2 EMISSIONS ARE BEING REDUCED; HOWEVER, SINCE THEIR NUMBER KEEPS GROWING FASTER AND FASTER, THE SAVINGS ARE IMMEDIATELY OFFSET OR EVEN EXCEEDED, SO WE MUST REMAIN VIGILANT.

EVERYONE, I.E. THE WHOLE OF SOCIETY, MUST ACCELERATE THE TRANSFORMATION INTO A SUSTAINABLE ECONOMY, BECAUSE YOU CAN'T NEGOTIATE WITH NATURE.

CHAPTER 5

TECHNICALLY, EVERYTHING IS POSSIBLE

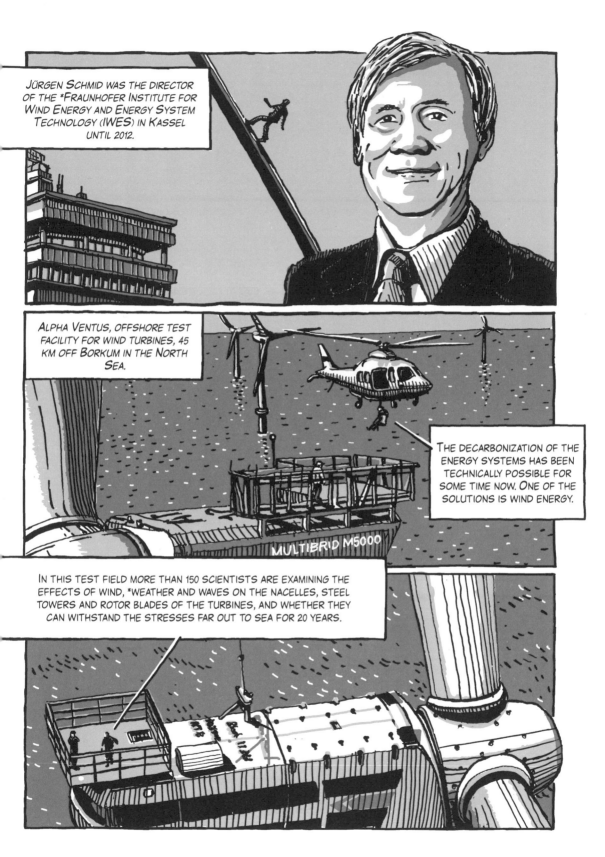

JÜRGEN SCHMID WAS THE DIRECTOR OF THE *FRAUNHOFER INSTITUTE FOR WIND ENERGY AND ENERGY SYSTEM TECHNOLOGY (IWES) IN KASSEL UNTIL 2012.

ALPHA VENTUS, OFFSHORE TEST FACILITY FOR WIND TURBINES, 45 KM OFF BORKUM IN THE NORTH SEA.

THE DECARBONIZATION OF THE ENERGY SYSTEMS HAS BEEN TECHNICALLY POSSIBLE FOR SOME TIME NOW. ONE OF THE SOLUTIONS IS WIND ENERGY.

IN THIS TEST FIELD MORE THAN 150 SCIENTISTS ARE EXAMINING THE EFFECTS OF WIND, *WEATHER AND WAVES ON THE NACELLES, STEEL TOWERS AND ROTOR BLADES OF THE TURBINES, AND WHETHER THEY CAN WITHSTAND THE STRESSES FAR OUT TO SEA FOR 20 YEARS.

MULTIBRID M5000

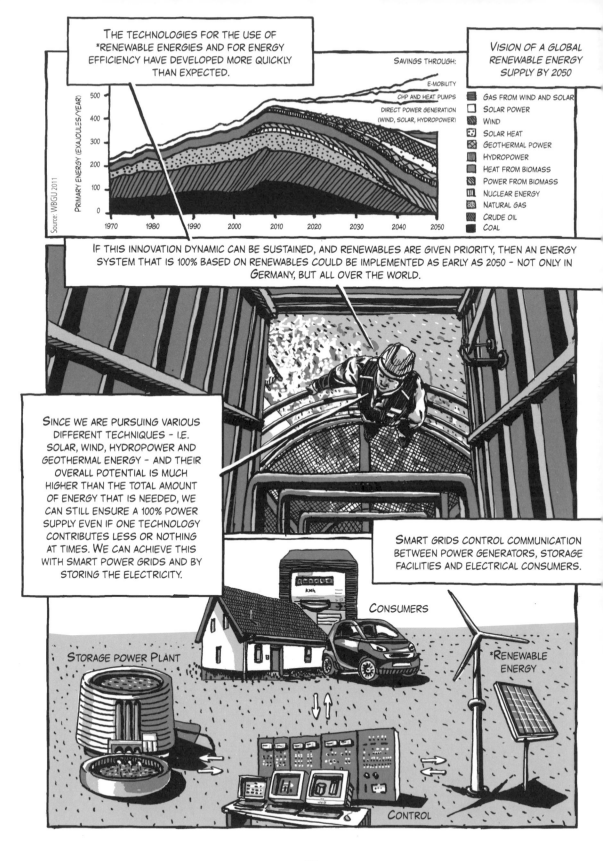

THE TECHNOLOGIES FOR THE USE OF *RENEWABLE ENERGIES AND FOR ENERGY EFFICIENCY HAVE DEVELOPED MORE QUICKLY THAN EXPECTED.

SAVINGS THROUGH:

E-MOBILITY
CHP AND HEAT PUMPS
DIRECT POWER GENERATION (WIND, SOLAR, HYDROPOWER)

VISION OF A GLOBAL RENEWABLE ENERGY SUPPLY BY 2050

GAS FROM WIND AND SOLAR
SOLAR POWER
WIND
SOLAR HEAT
GEOTHERMAL POWER
HYDROPOWER
HEAT FROM BIOMASS
POWER FROM BIOMASS
NUCLEAR ENERGY
NATURAL GAS
CRUDE OIL
COAL

PRIMARY ENERGY (EXAJOULES/YEAR)

500
400
300
200
100
0

1970 1980 1990 2000 2010 2020 2030 2040 2050

Source: WBGU 2011

IF THIS INNOVATION DYNAMIC CAN BE SUSTAINED, AND RENEWABLES ARE GIVEN PRIORITY, THEN AN ENERGY SYSTEM THAT IS 100% BASED ON RENEWABLES COULD BE IMPLEMENTED AS EARLY AS 2050 – NOT ONLY IN GERMANY, BUT ALL OVER THE WORLD.

SINCE WE ARE PURSUING VARIOUS DIFFERENT TECHNIQUES – I.E. SOLAR, WIND, HYDROPOWER AND GEOTHERMAL ENERGY – AND THEIR OVERALL POTENTIAL IS MUCH HIGHER THAN THE TOTAL AMOUNT OF ENERGY THAT IS NEEDED, WE CAN STILL ENSURE A 100% POWER SUPPLY EVEN IF ONE TECHNOLOGY CONTRIBUTES LESS OR NOTHING AT TIMES. WE CAN ACHIEVE THIS WITH SMART POWER GRIDS AND BY STORING THE ELECTRICITY.

SMART GRIDS CONTROL COMMUNICATION BETWEEN POWER GENERATORS, STORAGE FACILITIES AND ELECTRICAL CONSUMERS.

CONSUMERS

STORAGE POWER PLANT

*RENEWABLE ENERGY

CONTROL

62

THERE ARE TWO VIABLE TECHNOLOGIES FOR STORAGE. ONE OF THESE IS PUMPED STORAGE POWER PLANTS, WHICH HAS BEEN IN USE FOR SOME TIME.

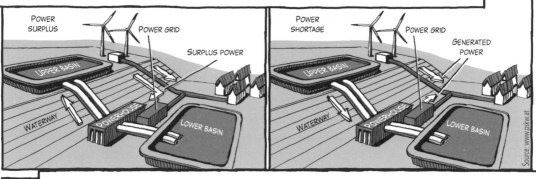

THE OTHER IS STORING THE ELECTRICITY IN THE FORM OF GAS. TOGETHER WITH THE CENTRE FOR SOLAR ENERGY AND HYDROGEN RESEARCH BADEN-WÜRTTEMBERG WE'RE DEVELOPING AN IDEA FOR COUPLING ELECTRICITY AND GAS.

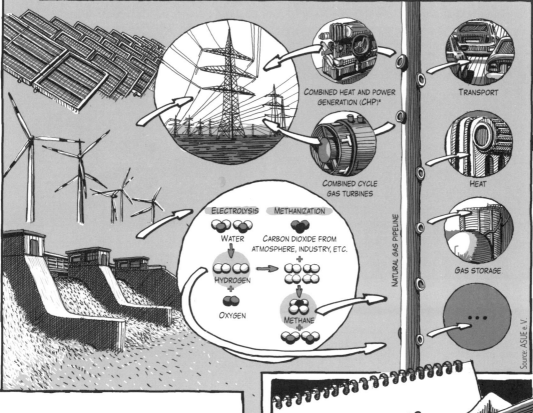

YOU TAKE THE EXCESS ENERGY FROM RENEWABLE SOURCES AND MAKE METHANE OUT OF IT. THIS GAS CAN BE USED TO GENERATE HEAT, OR AS A FUEL, OR BE STORED IN NATURAL GAS NETWORKS. THE NATURAL GAS NETWORKS ALREADY EXIST. THE METHANE CAN BE CONVERTED BACK INTO ELECTRICITY WHENEVER NECESSARY.

$$4H_2O \rightarrow 4H_2 + 2O_2$$
$$4H_2 + CO_2 \rightarrow CH_4 + 2H_2O$$

IN THIS PROCESS YOU ONLY RELEASE AS MUCH CO2 INTO THE ATMOSPHERE AS YOU PREVIOUSLY EXTRACTED FROM IT, MAKING THIS TECHNOLOGY CARBON NEUTRAL.

HOWEVER, WE MUST ALSO SAVE ENERGY. IN OTHER WORDS, WE NEED TO WORK ON BECOMING MORE ENERGY EFFICIENT, I.E. GETTING MORE OUT OF LESS.

YOU CAN ALSO REDUCE THE AMOUNT OF HEAT BEING GIVEN OFF INTO THE ATMOSPHERE BY INSULATING BUILDINGS BETTER; YOU THEN ALSO NEED LESS ENERGY TO HEAT THEM. A LOWER DEMAND FOR ENERGY AND THE USE OF LOW-CARBON OR RENEWABLE ENERGY CARRIERS LEAD TO A CONSIDERABLE REDUCTION IN CO_2 EMISSIONS.

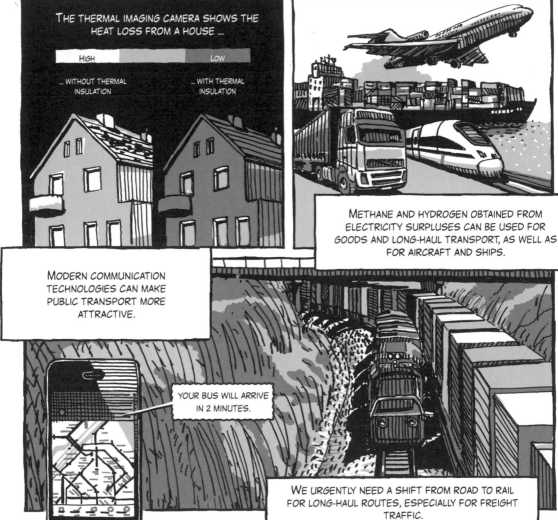

THE THERMAL IMAGING CAMERA SHOWS THE HEAT LOSS FROM A HOUSE ...

HIGH   LOW

... WITHOUT THERMAL INSULATION

... WITH THERMAL INSULATION

METHANE AND HYDROGEN OBTAINED FROM ELECTRICITY SURPLUSES CAN BE USED FOR GOODS AND LONG-HAUL TRANSPORT, AS WELL AS FOR AIRCRAFT AND SHIPS.

MODERN COMMUNICATION TECHNOLOGIES CAN MAKE PUBLIC TRANSPORT MORE ATTRACTIVE.

YOUR BUS WILL ARRIVE IN 2 MINUTES.

WE URGENTLY NEED A SHIFT FROM ROAD TO RAIL FOR LONG-HAUL ROUTES, ESPECIALLY FOR FREIGHT TRAFFIC.

HIGH-SPEED RAILWAY LINES CAN BE A GOOD ALTERNATIVE TO FLYING. IN ARIZONA THERE'S ALREADY A PROJECT FOR A COMPLETELY SOLAR-POWERED HIGH-SPEED TRAIN: THE SOLAR BULLET TRAIN.

AND OF COURSE WE MUST ALSO TRANSFORM PRIVATE TRANSPORT. ALL THE MAJOR CAR MAKERS HAVE – LONG SINCE – DEVELOPED PROTOTYPES FOR ENERGY-EFFICIENT ELECTRIC CARS AND OTHER CARS THAT USE LESS CARBON-INTENSIVE FUELS. THINGS MIGHT CHANGE IN THIS FIELD VERY SOON.

THE TESLA ROADSTER, THE FIRST FULLY ELECTRIC SPORTS CAR, IS VERY POPULAR, ESPECIALLY AMONG HOLLYWOOD STARS.

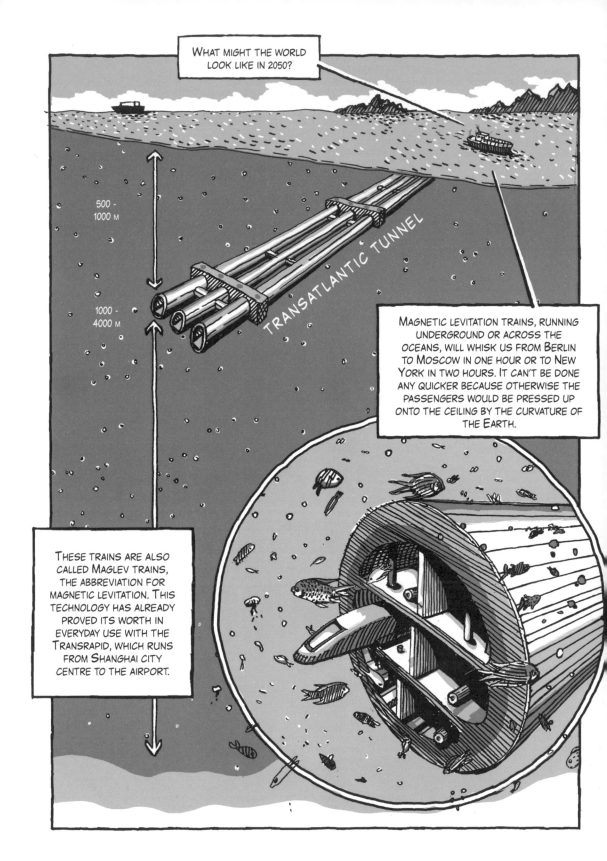

THE SAME PRINCIPLE APPLIES TO CARS IN CITY TRAFFIC. THEY ALSO USE MAGNETIC FORCES.

THE LINES CARRY THE ENERGY SUPPLY AND TRANSFER THE INFORMATION. THAT MEANS WE'RE CONNECTED ONLINE AND DON'T NEED TO STEER THE CAR ANY MORE. THE CAR FINDS THE DESTINATION BY ITSELF, WHICH HAS MANY BENEFITS, AS WE KNOW.

DRIVE ME HOME.

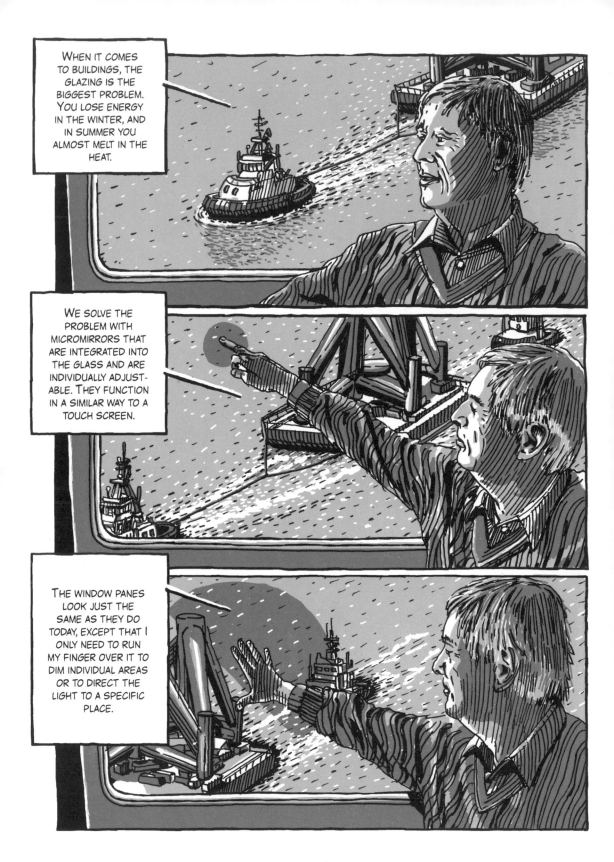

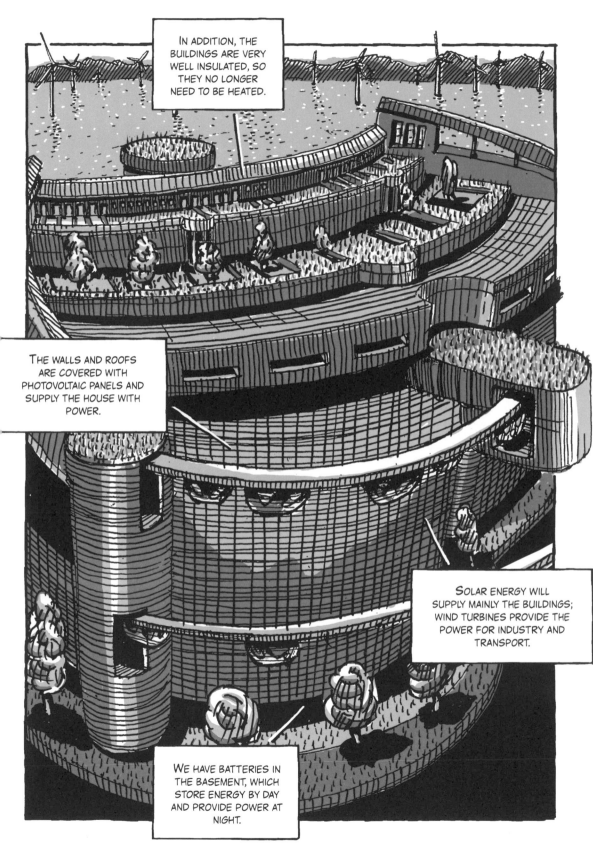

IN ADDITION, THE BUILDINGS ARE VERY WELL INSULATED, SO THEY NO LONGER NEED TO BE HEATED.

THE WALLS AND ROOFS ARE COVERED WITH PHOTOVOLTAIC PANELS AND SUPPLY THE HOUSE WITH POWER.

SOLAR ENERGY WILL SUPPLY MAINLY THE BUILDINGS; WIND TURBINES PROVIDE THE POWER FOR INDUSTRY AND TRANSPORT.

WE HAVE BATTERIES IN THE BASEMENT, WHICH STORE ENERGY BY DAY AND PROVIDE POWER AT NIGHT.

THE WIND TURBINES WILL NO LONGER BE ANCHORED TO THE SEABED, BUT WILL FLOAT FREELY ON THE OCEAN AND LOOK FOR THE BEST WIND.

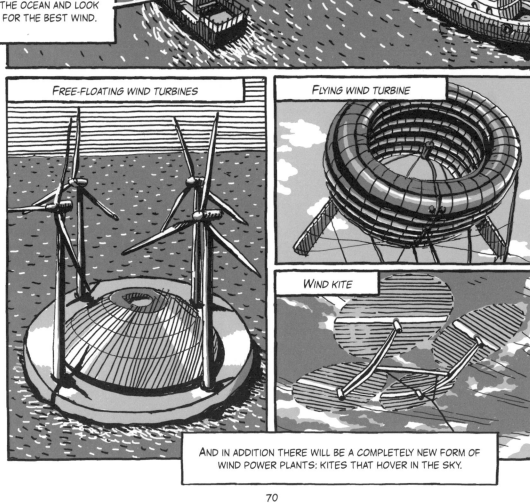

FREE-FLOATING WIND TURBINES

FLYING WIND TURBINE

WIND KITE

AND IN ADDITION THERE WILL BE A COMPLETELY NEW FORM OF WIND POWER PLANTS: KITES THAT HOVER IN THE SKY.

TELECOMMUNICATIONS WILL ALSO EVOLVE, OF COURSE. THIS IS THE MOST DIFFICULT AREA TO PREDICT, BECAUSE 40 YEARS IS AN IMMENSELY LONG PERIOD AT THE CURRENT RATE OF INNOVATION. WHAT IS CERTAIN IS THAT SMARTPHONES WILL BECOME MUCH MORE THE FOCUS OF COMMUNICATION.

A SHIP DOCKS IN BREMERHAVEN.

WE'LL HAVE ALL OUR IMPORTANT INFORMATION ON IT. FOR EXAMPLE, WE'LL BE ABLE TO CONTROL THE ENTIRE ENERGY MANAGEMENT OF OUR HOMES FROM OUR MOBILE PHONE.

*THE PROTESTERS' PLACARDS DEMAND A STOP TO THE OFFSHORE TERMINAL AND THE HARBOUR EXPANSION.

OF COURSE, ALL THIS IS ALSO GOOD FOR THE ECONOMY: BY THE MIDDLE OF THE CENTURY SEVERAL MILLION PEOPLE WILL BE WORKING IN THE NEWLY CREATED RENEWABLE ENERGY SECTOR. BUT AS ALWAYS, WHENEVER THERE ARE CHANGES, RESISTANCE WILL BE QUICK TO EVOLVE.

CHAPTER 6

A TASK FOR THE WHOLE WORLD

NEBOJSA NAKICENOVIC („NAKI"), IS A SYSTEMS ANALYST AND ENERGY ECONOMIST. HE LECTURES AT THE VIENNA UNIVERSITY OF TECHNOLOGY AND IS DEPUTY DIRECTOR GENERAL OF THE *INTERNATIONAL INSTITUTE FOR APPLIED SYSTEMS ANALYSIS (IIASA) IN LAXENBURG, AUSTRIA.

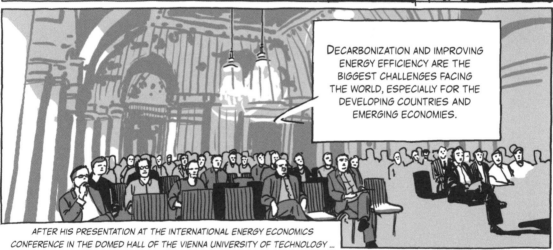

DECARBONIZATION AND IMPROVING ENERGY EFFICIENCY ARE THE BIGGEST CHALLENGES FACING THE WORLD, ESPECIALLY FOR THE DEVELOPING COUNTRIES AND EMERGING ECONOMIES.

AFTER HIS PRESENTATION AT THE INTERNATIONAL ENERGY ECONOMICS CONFERENCE IN THE DOMED HALL OF THE VIENNA UNIVERSITY OF TECHNOLOGY ...

... NAKI GIVES A UNIVERSITY LECTURE.

ABOUT 1.5 BILLION PEOPLE HAVE NO ACCESS TO ELECTRICITY TODAY.

EUROPE

KLICK!

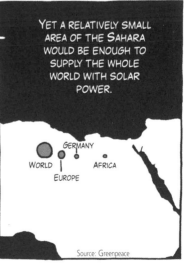

YET A RELATIVELY SMALL AREA OF THE SAHARA WOULD BE ENOUGH TO SUPPLY THE WHOLE WORLD WITH SOLAR POWER.

WORLD
GERMANY
EUROPE
AFRICA

Source: Greenpeace

AT THE IIASA WE CONCENTRATE ON PROBLEMS THAT ARE TOO BIG FOR A SINGLE COUNTRY TO COPE WITH ALONE. THE THREE MAIN PROBLEM AREAS ARE ENERGY AND CLIMATE CHANGE; FOOD AND WATER; POVERTY AND EQUITY.

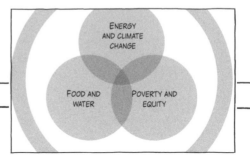

ENERGY AND CLIMATE CHANGE

FOOD AND WATER

POVERTY AND EQUITY

FOR OUR LONG-TERM STUDIES WE FEED OUR COMPUTERS WITH AS MUCH DATA AS POSSIBLE AND HAVE THEM CRUNCH NUMBERS ON A WIDE RANGE OF DIFFERENT FACTORS. THIS ENABLES US TO JUXTAPOSE A LOT OF DIFFERENT POSSIBLE FUTURE SCENARIOS.

GLOBAL PRIMARY ENERGY IN EXAJOULES (EJ)

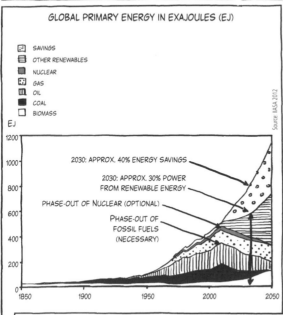

- SAVINGS
- OTHER RENEWABLES
- NUCLEAR
- GAS
- OIL
- COAL
- BIOMASS

Source: IIASA 2012

EJ

2030: APPROX. 40% ENERGY SAVINGS

2030: APPROX. 30% POWER FROM RENEWABLE ENERGY

PHASE-OUT OF NUCLEAR (OPTIONAL)

PHASE-OUT OF FOSSIL FUELS (NECESSARY)

1200
1000
800
600
400
200
0
1850   1900   1950   2000   2050

IN THIS WAY WE CAN GIVE POLICY-MAKERS A BASIS ON WHICH TO MAKE THE RIGHT DECISIONS.

THE CHART SHOWS HOW THE GLOBAL ENERGY SYSTEM WOULD NEED TO BE TRANSFORMED TO REACH THE GOALS OF THE *SUSTAINABLE ENERGY FOR ALL INITIATIVE, WHICH WAS LAUNCHED BY BAN KI-MOON, SECRETARY-GENERAL OF THE UNITED NATIONS.

THE INTERNATIONAL INSTITUTE FOR APPLIED SYSTEMS ANALYSIS IN LAXENBURG.

THE ELEMENTS OF OUR THREE PROBLEM AREAS ARE INTERDEPENDENT.

AN EXAMPLE: MORE AND MORE PEOPLE ARE MOVING TO THE CITIES. BY 2050, 80% OF ALL PEOPLE WILL LIVE IN URBAN AREAS, ALTHOUGH, INTERESTINGLY, THE BIRTH RATE IN THE COUNTRYSIDE IS MUCH HIGHER THAN IN THE CITY. THIS TREND PRIMARILY AFFECTS SOUTH ASIA, BUT ALSO AFRICA AND SOUTH AMERICA. USUALLY THERE IS NO REGULATED URBAN PLANNING AND OFTEN NOT EVEN HYGIENIC WASTE OR SEWAGE DISPOSAL, NOT TO MENTION THE LACK OF ELECTRICITY ACCESS.

MEXICO CITY 2012

FOR THIS ENORMOUS URBANIZATION WE NEED COMPLETELY NEW SOLUTIONS WHEN IT COMES TO SUPPLYING ENERGY. MINIMIZING CONSUMPTION AND CONVERTING THE TRANSPORT SYSTEM WILL PLAY AN ESSENTIAL ROLE IN THIS TRANSFORMATION. IN ORDER TO ACHIEVE THIS, WE NEED TRULY GLOBAL ENERGY NETWORKS, A *SUPER GRID, LIKE THE ONE THAT IS ALREADY PLANNED IN ASIA.

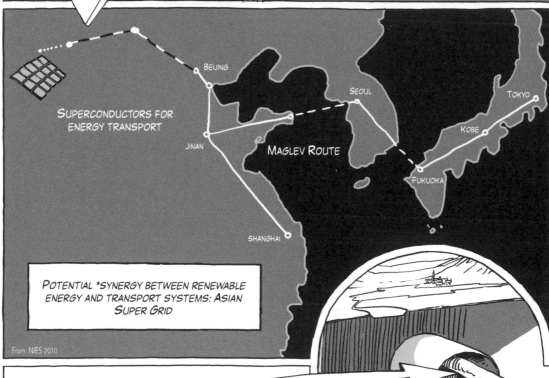

SUPERCONDUCTORS FOR ENERGY TRANSPORT

BEIJING

SEOUL

TOKYO

JINAN

MAGLEV ROUTE

KOBE

FUKUOKA

SHANGHAI

POTENTIAL *SYNERGY BETWEEN RENEWABLE ENERGY AND TRANSPORT SYSTEMS: ASIAN SUPER GRID

From: NIES 2010

From: EPRI 2010

WE ALSO PLACE A PIPELINE WITH CHILLED HYDROGEN OR METHANE NEXT TO THE TUBES FOR THE MAGLEV TRAINS. IT CONTAINS A SUPERCONDUCTOR IN WHICH ENERGY IN FORM OF ELECTRICITY AND HYDROGEN CAN BE TRANSPORTED OVER LARGE DISTANCES WITHOUT LOSSES. IN THIS WAY THE WHOLE WORLD COULD ALSO BE SUPPLIED WITH SOLAR ENERGY FROM THE DESERTS.

EUROPEAN DEVELOPMENT COOPERATION SHOULD GO BEYOND POVERTY REDUCTION AND FOCUS SYSTEMATICALLY ON THE GOAL OF LOW-CARBON DEVELOPMENT, CONTRIBUTING PRIMARILY TO THE CREATION OF CORRESPONDING INFRASTRUCTURES ESPECIALLY IN THE POOR DEVELOPING COUNTRIES. THIS WILL THEN ALSO PROMOTE GREEN GROWTH IN THESE COUNTRIES.

NAKI SETS OFF TO CAPE TOWN, SOUTH AFRICA, FOR THE FIRST STAKEHOLDER FORUM OF THE *AFRICA-EU ENERGY PARTNERSHIP. BY THE WAY, HE OFFSETS THE CO2 EMISSIONS OF HIS JOURNEY BY PURCHASING EMISSION PERMITS.

THE TOP PRIORITY IS THE PROVISION OF MODERN ENERGY SERVICES ALSO IN RURAL AREAS. IN THE COUNTRYSIDE WE NEED SMALLER LOCAL NETWORKS THAT CAN BE CONNECTED TO THE SUPER GRID.

THE WORLDWIDE NETWORK OF AIR ROUTES. THE LINES VISUALIZE THE AIR TRAFFIC BETWEEN THE 500 LARGEST AIRPORTS IN THE WORLD.

AT PRESENT IT IS MAINLY WOMEN WHO SPEND HOURS IN MANY COUNTRIES SEARCHING FOR FIREWOOD. THIS TIME IS THEN NOT AVAILABLE FOR OTHER WORK, WHICH EXACERBATES THE POVERTY EVEN MORE.

THE PEOPLE NEED LIGHT, NOT LEAST TO ADVANCE THEIR EDUCATION AND TRAINING. MANY HOUSEHOLDS USE SOLID FUELS FOR COOKING AND HEATING.

THE OPEN FIRES POLLUTE THE INDOOR AIR SO BADLY THAT IT CAUSES CONSIDERABLE HEALTH PROBLEMS. IT IS ESTIMATED THAT EACH YEAR 4 MILLION WOMEN AND CHILDREN ALL OVER THE WORLD DIE PREMATURELY AS A RESULT OF INHALING SMOKE GASES AND PARTICULATE MATTER DURING COOKING.

FORESTS ARE CUT DOWN TO OBTAIN FIREWOOD, WHICH LEADS TO EROSION, FLOODS AND, IN TURN, HARVEST LOSSES. IN ADDITION, CO_2 IS RELEASED, STRENGTHENING THE GREENHOUSE EFFECT; ITS IMPACT IN TURN FURTHER PREJUDICES THE HARVEST. CROP FAILURES EXACERBATE THE POVERTY, ...

... AND THE POVERTY MAKES IT IMPOSSIBLE TO SWITCH TO CLEAN ENERGY SOURCES, SINCE THE PEOPLE SIMPLY LACK THE MONEY TO BUY MODERN DEVICES. MOST DEVELOPING COUNTRIES DO IN FACT HAVE ENOUGH KNOW-HOW AND CAPITAL. BUT MUCH OF IT ENDS UP IN FOREIGN BANK ACCOUNTS. AND SINCE THERE ARE NO RELIABLE INSTITUTIONS, THE GENERAL CONDITIONS ARE NOT RIGHT FOR MAJOR INVESTMENTS.

ACCORDING TO UN NUTRITION EXPERT ARNOLD VAN HUIS, INSECTS SHOULD THEREFORE ALSO BE EATEN IN THE INDUSTRIALIZED NATIONS, BECAUSE REARING GRASSHOPPERS, CRICKETS AND MEALWORMS CONSUMES MUCH LESS RESOURCES THAN MEAT OR FISH PRODUCTION.

FOR US, IT'S STILL A TEST OF COURAGE TO EAT INSECTS. BUT THAT CAN CHANGE QUICKLY.

ABOUT A THOUSAND INSECT SPECIES ARE SUITABLE FOR HUMAN CONSUMPTION AND ARE TRADITIONALLY EATEN IN LARGE PARTS OF AFRICA, SOUTH EAST ASIA AND LATIN AMERICA. THAT'S WHY THE UN FOOD AND AGRICULTURE ORGANIZATION, THE *FAO, WOULD INITIALLY LIKE TO PROMOTE AN INSECT DIET IN THESE COUNTRIES.

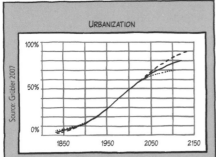

URBANIZATION

Source: Grübler 2007

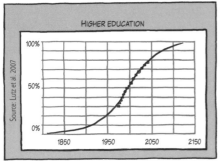

HIGHER EDUCATION

Source: Lutz et al. 2007

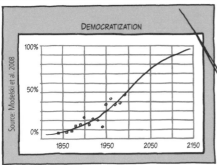

DEMOCRATIZATION

Source: Modelski et al. 2008

HOWEVER, THERE ARE ALSO POSITIVE DEVELOPMENTS AROUND THE WORLD. FOR EXAMPLE, ENVIRONMENTAL AWARENESS IS ON THE INCREASE, AND THE LONG-TERM POLITICAL TREND IS MOVING TOWARDS DEMOCRATIZATION. SUSTAINABLE DEVELOPMENT WILL ONLY BE POSSIBLE IF PEOPLE KNOW THAT THEIR VOTE CAN MAKE A DIFFERENCE.

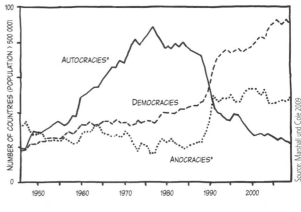

NUMBER OF COUNTRIES (POPULATION > 500 000)

AUTOCRACIES*

DEMOCRACIES

ANOCRACIES*

Source: Marshall und Cole 2009

IN ORDER TO ESTABLISH THE NEW ENERGY SYSTEMS AND INFRASTRUCTURES, WE NEED AT LEAST TWO COMPLEMENTARY EVOLUTIONS, ONE TECHNICAL AND ONE INSTITUTIONAL. AND PERHAPS A THIRD ONE RELATING TO OUR BEHAVIOUR.

NEW TECHNOLOGIES AND SYSTEMS WILL LEAD TO NEW BUSINESS MODELS AND INSTITUTIONAL MEASURES. ALL OF THESE PARALLEL AND COMPLEMENTARY TRANSFORMATIONS REQUIRE ECONOMIC, REGULATORY AND BEHAVIOURAL CHANGES TO DRIVE THEM FORWARD AT THE SAME TIME.

MANY COUNTRIES WILL LEAPFROG THE FOSSIL ENERGY ERA IN THEIR ECONOMIC DEVELOPMENT AND IMMEDIATELY ADOPT INNOVATIVE LOW-CARBON DEVELOPMENT PATHWAYS TOWARD A SUSTAINABLE ENERGY FUTURE.

CHAPTER 7

WHO IS GOING TO PAY FOR IT?

RENATE SCHUBERT IS A POLITICAL ECONOMIST AND DIRECTOR OF THE *INSTITUTE FOR ENVIRONMENTAL DECISIONS AT THE SWISS FEDERAL INSTITUTE OF TECHNOLOGY (ETH), ZURICH.

RENATE ON HER WAY TO GIVE A LECTURE

CLIMATE CHANGE INFLUENCES LIFE ALL OVER THE PLANET. ALL COUNTRIES ARE AFFECTED! THE MOST VULNERABLE – THE POOREST COUNTRIES AND POPULATIONS – SUFFER THE MOST, EVEN THOUGH THEY HAVE CONTRIBUTED THE LEAST TO CLIMATE CHANGE.

HOWEVER, THE COSTS CAUSED BY THE EXTREME WEATHER EVENTS ARE RISING IN ALL COUNTRIES, INCLUDING THE RICH ONES.

THE MAIN BUILDING OF ETH ZURICH

OVER THE NEXT FIVE YEARS, BAVARIA WILL SPEND MORE THAN €1 BILLION ON THE *ENERGIEWENDE AND CLIMATE PROTECTION, BECAUSE TEMPERATURES IN THE ALPS ARE RISING TWICE AS FAST AS THE GLOBAL AVERAGE AS A RESULT OF CLIMATE CHANGE.

BAVARIA'S ENVIRONMENT MINISTER MARCEL HUBER EXPECTS AVERAGE TEMPERATURES TO RISE BY 3-6°C BY THE YEAR 2100.

BECAUSE OF CLIMATE CHANGE, WE IN THE ALPS WILL HAVE TO RECKON WITH MORE FREQUENT TORRENTIAL RAIN, FLOODING AND LANDSLIDES THAN IN THE PAST. FURTHERMORE, THE REGION'S HIGHLY DIVERSE FLORA AND FAUNA ARE UNDER THREAT.

LANDSLIDE IN THE ALPS IN 2012. LANDSLIDES CAN TAKE THE FORM OF MUDFLOWS OR ROCK AVALANCHES. THEY CAUSE MORE DAMAGE THAN FLOODS.

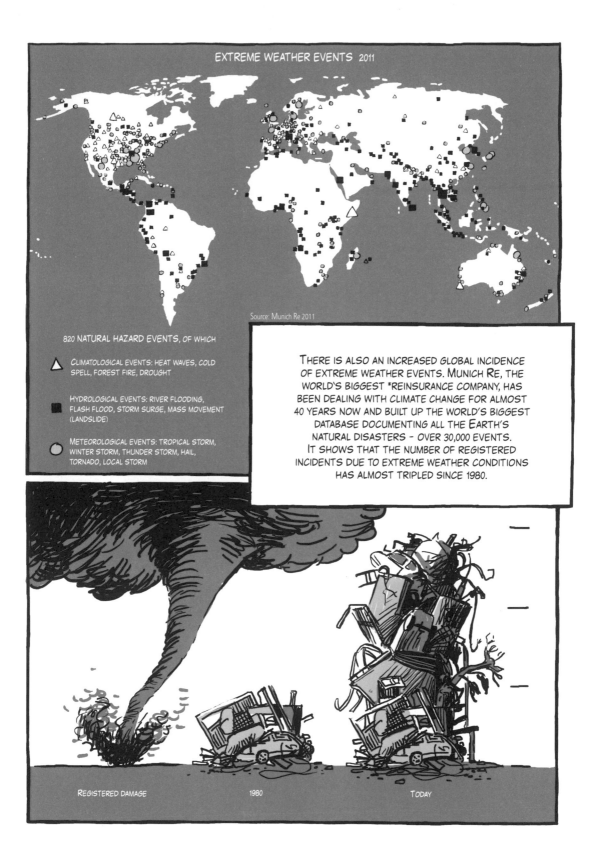

EXTREME WEATHER EVENTS 2011

Source: Munich Re 2011

820 NATURAL HAZARD EVENTS, OF WHICH

△ CLIMATOLOGICAL EVENTS: HEAT WAVES, COLD SPELL, FOREST FIRE, DROUGHT

■ HYDROLOGICAL EVENTS: RIVER FLOODING, FLASH FLOOD, STORM SURGE, MASS MOVEMENT (LANDSLIDE)

◗ METEOROLOGICAL EVENTS: TROPICAL STORM, WINTER STORM, THUNDER STORM, HAIL, TORNADO, LOCAL STORM

THERE IS ALSO AN INCREASED GLOBAL INCIDENCE OF EXTREME WEATHER EVENTS. MUNICH RE, THE WORLD'S BIGGEST *REINSURANCE COMPANY, HAS BEEN DEALING WITH CLIMATE CHANGE FOR ALMOST 40 YEARS NOW AND BUILT UP THE WORLD'S BIGGEST DATABASE DOCUMENTING ALL THE EARTH'S NATURAL DISASTERS – OVER 30,000 EVENTS. IT SHOWS THAT THE NUMBER OF REGISTERED INCIDENTS DUE TO EXTREME WEATHER CONDITIONS HAS ALMOST TRIPLED SINCE 1980.

REGISTERED DAMAGE   1980   TODAY

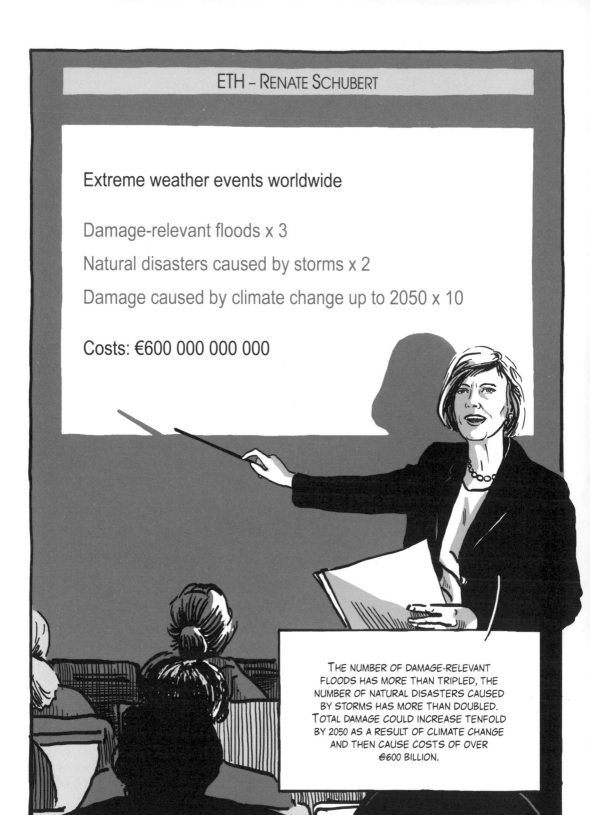

WE MUST REDUCE EMISSIONS OF GREENHOUSE GASES. IF WE CAN KEEP THE CONCENTRATION OF CO_2 IN THE ATMOSPHERE DOWN TO MAXIMUM OF 450 PPM, WE MIGHT MANAGE TO LIMIT GLOBAL WARMING TO 2°C. THAT WILL REQUIRE ENORMOUS INVESTMENT OVER THE NEXT FEW YEARS.

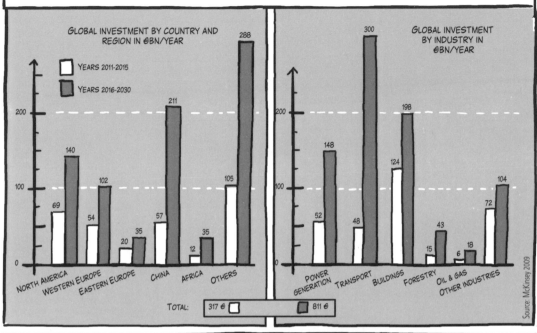

GLOBAL INVESTMENT BY COUNTRY AND REGION IN €BN/YEAR

☐ YEARS 2011-2015
☐ YEARS 2016-2030

GLOBAL INVESTMENT BY INDUSTRY IN €BN/YEAR

Source: McKinsey 2009

TOTAL: 317 € ☐   811 € ☐

ON THE WAY TO THE CANTEEN AT THE ETH

NECESSARY INVESTMENT

UP TO 2015
317

AFTER 2026
811

BILLIONS OF €PER

YEAR

SO IN THIS DECADE WE URGENTLY NEED TO INVEST IN RESEARCH AND DEVELOPMENT FOR NEW TECHNOLOGIES IN THE ENERGY SECTOR AND IN THE FIELDS OF MOBILITY, HOUSING, LAND USE AND COMMUNICATION.

IF WE POSTPONE THE TRANSFORMATION, THE COSTS WILL ONLY INCREASE FURTHER, BECAUSE EVEN MORE DRASTIC MEASURES TO REDUCE GREENHOUSE-GAS EMISSIONS WILL THEN BE NEEDED IN A SHORTER PERIOD OF TIME. WE ESTIMATE THAT A POSTPONEMENT OF ONLY ANOTHER 10 YEARS WOULD INCREASE THE COSTS BY MORE THAN 46%.

**Note: The amount of electricity specified here is not fully used by the final consumer, because the conventional power plants also need electricity to function, and a certain percentage is always lost, both when transporting electricity and when electricity is converted into heat and lighting, etc.

A FURTHER RECOMMENDATION IS THE MOBILIZATION OF PRIVATE CAPITAL. BANKS SHOULD OFFER FUNDS THAT ENABLE PRIVATE INVESTORS TO PARTICIPATE IN PROJECTS FOR SUSTAINABLE ENERGY SYSTEMS. IF ONLY A SMALL PROPORTION OF THE WORLD'S EXISTING PRIVATE ASSETS WERE USED FOR THE TRANSFORMATION OF THE ENERGY SYSTEMS, THE INVESTMENT COULD BE EASILY FINANCED.

SOME EMERGING ECONOMIES, PARTICULARLY CHINA, HAVE SUFFICIENT PUBLIC FUNDS AND LARGE FOREIGN EXCHANGE RESERVES, WHICH COULD BE USED TO FINANCE THE NECESSARY UPFRONT INVESTMENT. SO, COMPARED TO THE HIGHLY INDEBTED INDUSTRIALIZED COUNTRIES, FINANCIALLY THEY HAVE A HEAD START FOR CONVERTING THEIR ENERGY SYSTEM.

PERCENTAGE DISTRIBUTION OF GLOBAL FOREIGN EXCHANGE RESERVES, 2010

OTHERS 55,2%

CHINA 29,5%

JAPAN 12,3%

USA 0,5%

GERMANY 0,5%

ITALY 0,4%

FRANCE 0,3%

Sources: World Gold Council, Bloomberg

AND MEASURES TO COMBAT CLIMATE CHANGE CREATE IMPORTANT BUSINESS OPPORTUNITIES, BECAUSE NEW MARKETS ARE CREATED FOR GOODS, ENERGY TECHNOLOGIES AND SERVICES THAT ARE PRODUCED WITH LOW CARBON EMISSIONS.

RENEWABLE ENERGY:
381,600 JOBS IN 2011

NUMBER OF JOBS BY INDUSTRY

SOLAR ENERGY
125 000 (33%)

BIOENERGY
124 400 (33%)

WIND ENERGY
101 100 (26%)

GEOTHERMAL ENERGY
14 200 (4%)

HYDRO POWER
7300 (2%)

PUBLIC/COMMUNITY FUNDED
9600 (3%)

Data: DLR/DIW/ZSW/GWS/Prognos 2012

THESE MARKETS CAN GROW TO VALUES OF HUNDREDS OF BILLIONS OF EUROS PER YEAR, AND EMPLOYMENT CAN EXPAND ACCORDINGLY IN THESE SECTORS. IN THE LONG TERM, FIGHTING CLIMATE CHANGE MEANS GROWTH – BOTH FOR RICH AND POOR COUNTRIES.

CHAPTER 8

THE STATE ALSO HAS A ROLE TO PLAY

SABINE SCHLACKE TEACHES PUBLIC LAW AT THE UNIVERSITY OF BREMEN, FOCUSING ON GERMAN, EUROPEAN AND INTERNATIONAL ENVIRONMENTAL AND ADMINISTRATIVE LAW.

UNIVERSITY CAMPUS

TO ENABLE THE NEW MARKETS FOR SUSTAINABLE PRODUCTS AND TECHNOLOGIES TO DEVELOP, A REGULATORY FRAMEWORK IS NEEDED TO GIVE INVESTORS CONFIDENCE.

WE NEED A PROACTIVE STATE THAT LAYS DOWN NOT ONLY AMBITIOUS, BUT ALSO BINDING AND LONG-TERM TARGETS.

ONE OF THE STATE'S FUNDAMENTAL TASKS IS TO ENSURE THAT ITS CITIZENS HAVE CLEAN AIR AND SAFE DRINKING WATER, THAT SCHOOLS AND TRANSPORT SYSTEMS ARE BUILT, AND THAT THE ECOSYSTEM CAN FUNCTION EFFECTIVELY.

SABINE CYCLES PAST THE UNIVERSUM BREMEN SCIENCE MUSEUM ON THE WAY TO HER OFFICE.

BEES POLLINATING FLOWERS – ESSENTIAL FOR OUR FOOD PRODUCTION – CAN BE REGARDED AS AN *ECOSYSTEM SERVICE. WHEN THE CLIMATE CHANGES, THE VEGETATION CHANGES, TOO. ALONGSIDE MANY OTHER FACTORS, THIS MAY BE ONE REASON FOR HIGH LEVELS OF BEE MORTALITY, WHICH IS ALREADY A GLOBAL PROBLEM.

SO IT WOULD SHOW CONSISTENCY TO EXPLICITLY ENSHRINE CLIMATE PROTECTION AS A NATIONAL OBJECTIVE IN THE GERMAN BASIC LAW AND AS A GOAL OF THE EUROPEAN UNION.

CAMPAIGN OF THE *GLOBAL 2000 ORGANIZATION IN AUSTRIA

Klimaschutz zum Staatsziel machen*

GLOBAL 2000

THIS WOULD CREATE CONFIDENCE AND PROMOTE A WILLINGNESS TO INVEST IN NEW TECHNOLOGIES. BUT OF COURSE WE ALSO NEED SPECIFIC LEGAL INSTRUMENTS FOR THE IMPLEMENTATION OF CLIMATE PROTECTION MEASURES.

*MAKE CLIMATE PROTECTION A NATIONAL OBJECTIVE

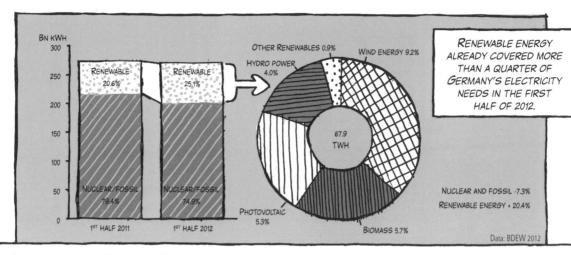

BN KWH

RENEWABLE 20.6%

NUCLEAR/FOSSIL 79.4%

1ST HALF 2011

RENEWABLE 25.1%

NUCLEAR/FOSSIL 74.9%

1ST HALF 2012

OTHER RENEWABLES 0.9%
HYDRO POWER 4.0%
WIND ENERGY 9.2%

67.9 TWH

PHOTOVOLTAIC 5.3%

BIOMASS 5.7%

RENEWABLE ENERGY ALREADY COVERED MORE THAN A QUARTER OF GERMANY'S ELECTRICITY NEEDS IN THE FIRST HALF OF 2012.

NUCLEAR AND FOSSIL -7.3%
RENEWABLE ENERGY + 20.4%

Data: BDEW 2012

GERMANY HAS THE *RENEWABLE ENERGY ACT. IT HAS BEEN PROMOTING RENEWABLE ENERGIES FOR 20 YEARS BY GIVING PRIORITY TO FEEDING ELECTRICITY FROM RENEWABLE SOURCES INTO THE GRID AT A GUARANTEED PRICE. AND SHOULD THERE BE ANY CHANGES IN THE LAW IN THE FUTURE, THE CURRENT REGULATION WILL CONTINUE TO APPLY FOR PLANTS INSTALLED UNDER THE OLD RULES. THIS CREATES INVESTMENT SECURITY.

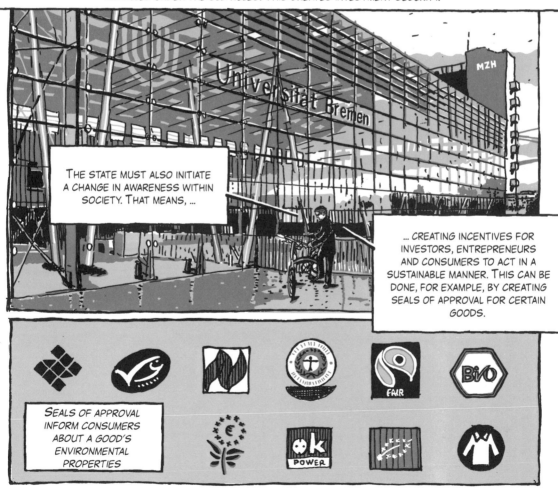

THE STATE MUST ALSO INITIATE A CHANGE IN AWARENESS WITHIN SOCIETY. THAT MEANS, ...

... CREATING INCENTIVES FOR INVESTORS, ENTREPRENEURS AND CONSUMERS TO ACT IN A SUSTAINABLE MANNER. THIS CAN BE DONE, FOR EXAMPLE, BY CREATING SEALS OF APPROVAL FOR CERTAIN GOODS.

SEALS OF APPROVAL INFORM CONSUMERS ABOUT A GOOD'S ENVIRONMENTAL PROPERTIES

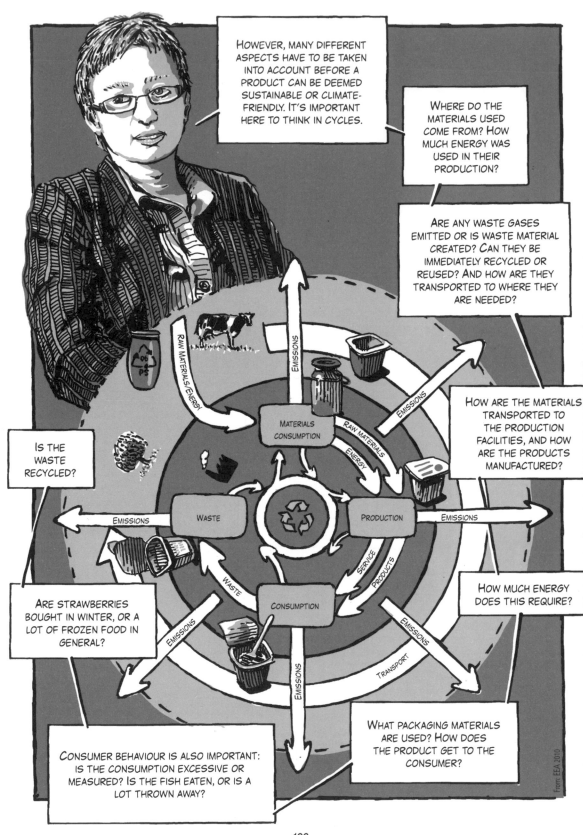

SABINE, THE JOURNALIST FROM RADIO BREMEN IS ON THE PHONE. HE WANTS TO TALK ABOUT YOUR ARTICLE ON EMISSIONS TRADING.

AS FAR AS COMPANIES ARE CONCERNED, THE MOST IMPORTANT POLITICAL MEASURE ON CLIMATE-FRIENDLINESS IS TO ENFORCE A PRICE FOR CO_2 EMISSIONS; THAT IS THE BASIS OF THE EMISSIONS TRADING SCHEME. IT IS ABSOLUTELY NECESSARY FOR THE GREAT TRANSFORMATION TOWARDS SUSTAINABILITY.

EMISSIONS TRADING, WHICH IS ALREADY PRACTISED IN THE EU, WORKS LIKE THIS: THE EU MEMBER STATES ALLOCATE TO COMPANIES THE RIGHT TO EMIT A CERTAIN AMOUNT OF GREENHOUSE GASES INTO THE ATMOSPHERE.

IF A COMPANY REDUCES ITS GREENHOUSE-GAS EMISSIONS, IT CAN THEN SELL SOME OF ITS RIGHTS IN THE FORM OF CERTIFICATES TO ANOTHER COMPANY THAT HAS MORE EMISSIONS THAN CERTIFICATES.

11.05.12 DIE WELT *Forschungsergebnisse*

ALLERGIE-BOOM IN DEUTSCHLAND
ERDERWÄRMUNG SORGT FÜR LÄNGERE POLLENPLAGE

NEWSPAPER HEADLINE IN 'DIE WELT' ON 5 NOV. 2012: THE COSTS TO THE HEALTHCARE SYSTEM ARE ON THE INCREASE.

SUCH A TRADING SYSTEM WILL ONLY FUNCTION IN THE LONG TERM IF THE PRICE OF CO_2 EMISSIONS COVERS THE REAL COST TO SOCIETY, I.E. ALSO THE FOLLOW-UP COSTS. THE EXAMPLE OF EMISSIONS TRADING ALREADY SHOWS THAT WE MUST NO LONGER ONLY THINK AND PLAN NATIONALLY, BUT EUROPE-WIDE AND INTERNATIONALLY. INCIDENTALLY, THIS IS ALSO NECESSARY IN THE PLANNING OF INFRASTRUCTURES SUCH AS ELECTRICITY GRIDS.

HOWEVER, INTERNATIONAL PLANNING REQUIRES LARGE-SCALE AND OFTEN LENGTHY COORDINATION PROCESSES, WHICH STAND IN THE WAY OF RAPID ACTION. SUCH BLOCKAGES AND OBSTACLES HAVE TO BE OVERCOME. BUT IT IS POSSIBLE, AS WAS SHOWN BY THE RAPID EU-WIDE BANK RESCUE SCHEMES DURING THE 2009 CRISIS.

BANK

ANOTHER DIFFICULTY IS THAT POLITICS IN DEMOCRACIES IS LOCKED INTO RELATIVELY SHORT ELECTORAL CYCLES, SO THAT QUICK-FIXES AND MEDIAGENIC MEASURES ARE OFTEN POPULAR WITH VOTERS. WORKING TOWARDS LONG-TERM OBJECTIVES IS LESS ATTRACTIVE BY COMPARISON.

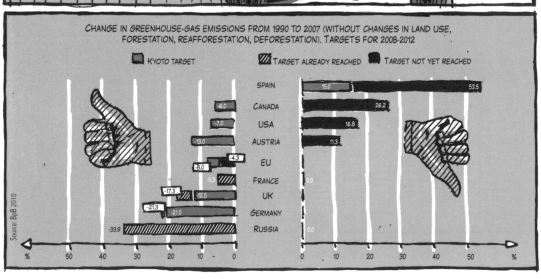

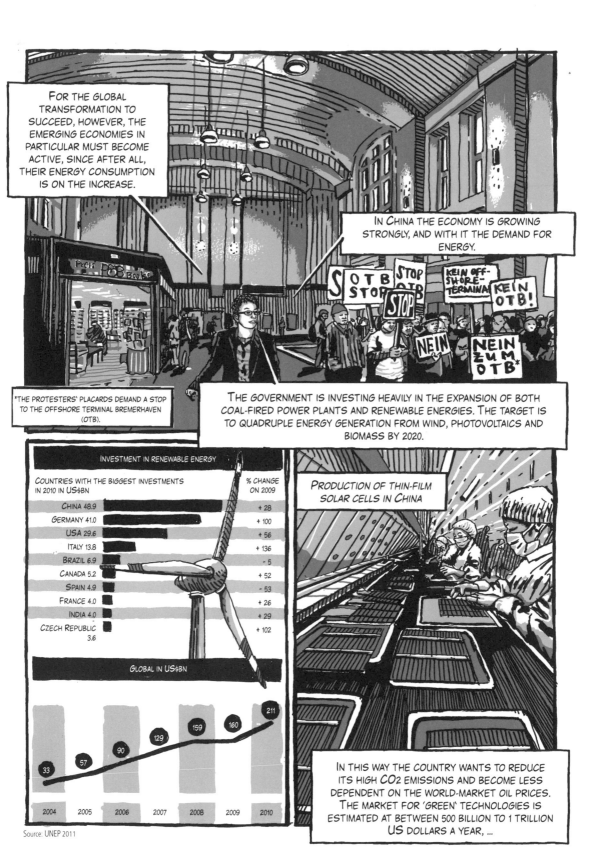

SABINE VISITS THE PLANNED *OFFSHORE TERMINAL BREMERHAVEN (OTB)* FOR WIND TURBINES.

OTB

... HOWEVER, SUCH MEASURES DO NOT SEEM TO BE VERY POPULAR AMONG THE CHINESE POPULATION, BECAUSE THEY SEE IT AS A GROWTH INHIBITOR. FURTHERMORE, IT'S BECOMING MORE AND MORE DIFFICULT TO ENFORCE DECISIONS ORDERED BY THE CENTRAL GOVERNMENT AT THE LOCAL AND REGIONAL LEVEL.

SHE TAKES A LOOK AT THE EXISTING LADING PORT.

THE SITUATION IN BRAZIL IS COMPLETELY DIFFERENT. THE POLITICAL LEGITIMACY OF 'GREEN' TECHNOLOGIES AND THEIR ACCEPTANCE BY THE POPULATION HAVE BEEN INCREASING CONTINUOUSLY OVER THE LAST 20 YEARS. THE COUNTRY ALREADY COVERS 40% OF ITS ENERGY NEEDS FROM RENEWABLE SOURCES – PRIMARILY HYDROPOWER.

ITAIPÚ HYDROELECTRIC POWER STATION

SO BRAZIL HAS ALREADY MADE A LOT OF PROGRESS IN CLIMATE-FRIENDLY POWER GENERATION. UNFORTUNATELY, THINGS LOOK DIFFERENT WHEN IT COMES TO THE CONSERVATION OF BIODIVERSITY AND, IN PARTICULAR, THE RAINFOREST.

SOYA FIELDS IN MATO GROSSE STATE

THE HITHERTO MOST BIODIVERSE COUNTRY IN THE WORLD IS STILL DOING TOO LITTLE TO FIGHT DEFORESTATION AND SLASH-AND-BURN FARMING, WITH THE RESULT THAT IT EMITS A CONSIDERABLE PERCENTAGE OF THE GREENHOUSE GASES IT SAVES BACK INTO THE ATMOSPHERE.

INDIA, WITH OVER A BILLION INHABITANTS, WAS STILL PRODUCING MORE THAN HALF OF ITS ELECTRICITY IN OUTDATED COAL-FIRED POWER PLANTS IN 2006. THE ELECTRICITY GRID IS AILING, AND COUNTLESS VILLAGES ARE STILL NOT CONNECTED TO THE CENTRAL MAINS.

DISTRIBUTION OF RENEWABLE ENERGY
2006-2007

● SMALL HYDROPOWER PLANTS UP TO 25 MEGAWATT

□ BIOMASS

▲ WIND POWER

From: MNRE 2006/7

LOCALLY GENERATED RENEWABLE ENERGIES SEEM THE PERFECT SOLUTION TO PROVIDE POWER FOR THE FAST-GROWING ECONOMY.

THE COUNTRY RECOGNIZED THE STRATEGIC IMPORTANCE OF RENEWABLE ENERGIES AT AN EARLY STAGE AND CREATED A MINISTRY OF NON-CONVENTIONAL ENERGY SOURCES IN 1992. THE GOVERNMENT PROMOTES RESEARCH AND DEVELOPMENT OF NEW TECHNOLOGIES IN THE ENERGY SECTOR, AND INDIA HAS SIGNED UP TO THE KYOTO PROTOCOL.

SABINE MEETS PROTESTERS AT THE HARBOUR.

THE HARBOUR EXPANSION IS DESTROYING AN IMPORTANT NATURE RESERVE. WE WANT TO PREVENT THAT.

WHAT DO THEY WANT TO ACHIEVE EXACTLY?

THIS EXAMPLE SHOWS THAT CLIMATE PROTECTION CAN ALSO COME INTO CONFLICT WITH ECOLOGICAL GOALS. THE STATE MUST TAKE THESE CONFLICTS SERIOUSLY. IN THIS CONTEXT, THE LAW CAN PROVIDE A MECHANISM FOR BALANCING INTERESTS. WITHOUT PUBLIC OPINION, WITHOUT THE PARTICIPATION OF THE POPULATION, THE AIM OF CREATING A SOCIETY WITH A SUSTAINABLE AND LOW-CARBON ECONOMY WILL NOT SUCCEED ANYWHERE.

CHAPTER 9

POLITICIANS CAN'T MANAGE IT ALONE

CLAUS LEGGEWIE IS A POLITICAL SCIENTIST AND DIRECTOR OF THE *INSTITUTE FOR ADVANCED STUDY IN THE HUMANITIES IN ESSEN (GERMANY).

IN ORDER TO ACHIEVE THE GREAT TRANSFORMATION WE WOULD ALL HAVE TO RECONSIDER OUR VALUES. UNFORTUNATELY, WE ARE DEALING WITH A STRONG FORCE OF INERTIA HERE, OUR 'INNER BEAST'!

COAL FOR BBQ ONLY!

ENERGIEWENDE NOW!

EATING VEGETARIAN FOR A CHANGE FROM TIME TO TIME IS NO BIG SACRIFICE, BUT IT OFFERS AN OPPORTUNITY NOT ONLY TO EAT MORE HEALTHILY, BUT ALSO TO ACT SUSTAINABLY AND DO SOMETHING TO PROTECT THE CLIMATE AT THE SAME TIME.

TELL ME, YOU REALLY DON'T EAT MEAT AT ALL? AND YOU'RE SURE YOU'RE NOT LACKING ANYTHING?

THERE'S NO POINT IN ANY GOVERNMENT PASSING A LAW MAKING ALL CITIZENS VEGETARIANS. THAT WOULD BE A DICTATORSHIP OF VIRTUE. BUT THE STATE COULD LAUNCH A CAMPAIGN OF PERSUASION TO GENERATE INTEREST IN NEW IDEAS, SHOW THE OPPORTUNITIES OF SUCH A TRANSFORMATION, AND LINK IT WITH IDEAS OF A GOOD LIFE WHICH THE MAJORITY OF THE PEOPLE ALREADY HAVE ANYWAY.

AT THE ADVERTISING AGENCY

OK, LET ME TALK TO HIM.

MR RUDOLF, IT'S THE ENVIRONMENT MINISTRY ... THEY WANT TO START A CAMPAIGN ON VEGETARIAN FOOD.

MY APPROACH IS TO SHOW THAT THE BIGGEST ANIMALS ARE HERBIVORES. THAT'LL BE A REAL EYE-CATCHER!

WE'LL BE LAUNCHING IN ALL THE MAIN CITIES SIMULTANEOUSLY; WE MUST SWIM WITH THE SOCIAL STREAM.

THE BIGGEST ANIMALS ONLY EAT VEGETABLES

DEMOCRATIC LEGITIMACY IS MORE THAN JUST GAINING ACCEPTANCE. APART FROM THE OUTPUT, I.E. THE PRACTICAL RESULTS OF POLITICS FOR THE CITIZENS, IT ALWAYS INVOLVES INPUT TOO: NAMELY THE POPULATION'S PARTICIPATION IN THE DECISIONS. IN A DEMOCRACY THIS IS DONE BY ACTIVE MAJORITY CONSENT TO AN ISSUE, E.G. IN ELECTIONS OR REFERENDA.

PARTICIPATION IS THE BEST WAY TO GAIN LEGITIMACY FROM THE POPULATION. WHEN PEOPLE ACTIVELY TAKE PART IN POLITICAL DECISION-MAKING PROCESSES – WHETHER BY SIGNING A PETITION OR JOINING A CITIZENS' ACTION GROUP – THEY ARE INVOLVED AS ACTORS. THEY PARTICIPATE IN DECISION-MAKING PROCESSES, UNDERSTAND THEM AND ARE THEN WILLING TO GIVE THEM THEIR SUPPORT.

*SAVE THE PRINCESS GARDENS (AN URBAN GARDENING PROJECT)

INDEED, THERE HAVE BEEN TRENDS WITHIN THE POPULATION IN FAVOUR OF SUSTAINABILITY AND A CLIMATE-FRIENDLY LIFESTYLE FOR A LONG TIME. ITS SUPPORTERS ARE NOT – OR NO LONGER – GOING AGAINST THE TIDE. THIS TREND CAN BE OBSERVED ACROSS CULTURES, EVEN WORLDWIDE.

IN SPAIN, FOR EXAMPLE, ALMOST 100% OF THE POPULATION TAKE CLIMATE CHANGE VERY SERIOUSLY AS A GLOBAL ENVIRONMENTAL PROBLEM.

BASIC NEEDS LIKE SHELTER AND FOOD SECURITY MUST BE ADEQUATELY MET BEFORE POST-MATERIALIST VALUES AND AN ORIENTATION TOWARDS SUSTAINABILITY CAN BECOME THE NORM. THEN, QUALITATIVE NEEDS – SUCH AS EDUCATION, LIVING IN HARMONY WITH NATURE, LEISURE – BECOME MORE IMPORTANT, AND SO-CALLED GROWTH TARGETS (MORE MONEY AND MORE MATERIAL GOODS) BECOME LESS ATTRACTIVE.

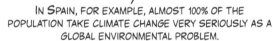

SERIOUSLY / VERY SERIOUSLY

NOT VERY SERIOUSLY / NOT AT ALL SERIOUSLY

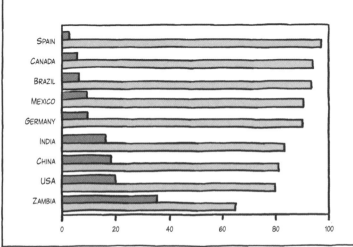

Source: World Values Survey 2009

THIS BECOMES ESPECIALLY CLEAR WHEN IT COMES TO YOUR DIET: IT'S NOT A MATTER OF EATING AS MUCH AS POSSIBLE, ...

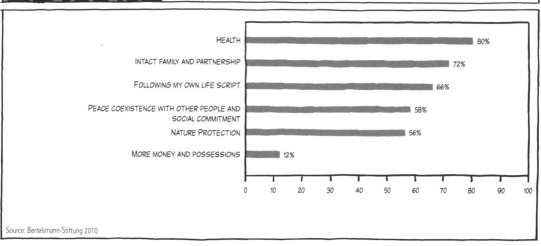

... BUT OF EATING AS WELL AS POSSIBLE AND TAKING CARE NOT TO HARM YOURSELF OR OTHERS WITH YOUR EATING HABITS.

THE PURSUIT OF HAPPINESS INVOLVES INTANGIBLE FACTORS LIKE BEING EMBEDDED IN COMMUNITIES AND NETWORKS, PARTICULARLY FAMILIES. BUT FULFILLING LEISURE TIME IS ALSO IMPORTANT. THIS HAS BEEN SHOWN BY STUDIES IN THE PAST FEW YEARS.

HEALTH	80%
INTACT FAMILY AND PARTNERSHIP	72%
FOLLOWING MY OWN LIFE SCRIPT	66%
PEACE COEXISTENCE WITH OTHER PEOPLE AND SOCIAL COMMITMENT	58%
NATURE PROTECTION	56%
MORE MONEY AND POSSESSIONS	12%

Source: Bertelsmann-Stiftung 2010

For me, a 'good life' means not only following my own life script – which is a good start – but also taking on responsibility for others and for future generations. In other words, not to live in an 'other-directed' and egoistic way, but in a way that is compatible with my environment. Smartphones, for example, are very popular. And that's a good thing because they encourage communication, knowledge sharing, participation and transparency. But must it always be the very latest model? Smartphone manufacture puts a lot of pressure on the environment, and there is hardly any recycling.

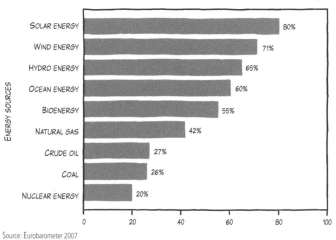

ACCEPTANCE OF DIFFERENT ENERGY CARRIERS IN THE EU,
ATTITUDES AS %

Energy Sources	%
SOLAR ENERGY	80%
WIND ENERGY	71%
HYDRO ENERGY	65%
OCEAN ENERGY	60%
BIOENERGY	55%
NATURAL GAS	42%
CRUDE OIL	27%
COAL	26%
NUCLEAR ENERGY	20%

Source: Eurobarometer 2007

CHANGING VALUES DO NOT, HOWEVER, MEAN THAT THESE NEW ATTITUDES ARE TRANSLATED ONE-TO-ONE INTO ACTION. IT'S BY NO MEANS RARE FOR PEOPLE TO ADVOCATE AMBITIOUS CLIMATE PROTECTION IN SURVEYS WHILE AT THE SAME TIME REJECTING HIGHER PRICES FOR ELECTRICITY AND FOSSIL FUELS.

SO THERE IS ONLY A WEAK CORRELATION BETWEEN ATTITUDES AND BEHAVIOUR.

JUTE, NOT PLASTIC? NEVER HEARD THAT ONE BEFORE!

CHANGE AGENTS CAN HELP OVERCOME THESE BARRIERS; THEY CAN SET A PROCESS IN MOTION THAT LEADS NOT FROM KNOWLEDGE TO ACTION, BUT FROM ACTION TO KNOWLEDGE.

TAKE URBAN GARDENERS, FOR EXAMPLE. A FEW PEOPLE START GROWING HERBS AND VEGETABLES ON UNUSED BROWNFIELD SITES IN THE CITY. OTHER JOIN IN AND HELP OR BUY PRODUCE THERE. OR JUST DRINK A CUP OF COFFEE.

ONE CAN FIND OUT ABOUT DIFFERENT POTATO VARIETIES THAT WERE ALMOST FORGOTTEN AND ARE NOW BEING REDISCOVERED, OR ABOUT OLD AND NEW COMPOSTING METHODS, OR BEE KEEPING IN THE CITY, WHICH IS CURRENTLY EXPERIENCING A RENAISSANCE. THEY WILL START THINKING ABOUT THEIR OWN DIET AND HOW THEIR FOOD IS PRODUCED.

PRINCESS GARDENS IN THE KREUZBERG DISTRICT OF BERLIN

AT THE SAME TIME THEY ARE ACTIVELY TURNING PART OF THEIR CITY INTO A GARDEN, GETTING TO KNOW EACH OTHER, EXCHANGING IDEAS AND ABOVE ALL HAVING FUN TOGETHER.

WE WANT TO SHOW THAT A CITY CAN ALSO LOOK DIFFERENT: GREEN, DIVERSE, URBAN, DESIGNED BY US AND WELL-PREPARED FOR THE CHALLENGES OF THE FUTURE.

THERE'S NO DOGMA INVOLVED; IT'S ABOUT PEOPLE CREATING A PLACE WITH THEIR OWN HANDS THAT BRINGS THEM TOGETHER AND ENRICHES THEIR LIVES.

CHANGE AGENTS: ROBERT AND MARCO, OPERATORS OF THE GARDEN

THESE PEOPLE ARE PIONEERS, LEADERS OF SOCIAL CHANGE. CHANGE AGENTS ARE OF KEY IMPORTANCE IN THE INTRODUCTION OF NEW TECHNOLOGIES AND IDEAS. THEY ARE TREND SETTERS, AND THEY CREATE A WE-FEELING.

WISE LEGISLATION, TARGETED MARKET INCENTIVES, COMPANY INITIATIVES AND FAR-SIGHTED INVESTMENTS CAN ALL REINFORCE THE TREND. PAYING ATTENTION TO YOUR OWN DIET AND HOW FOOD IS PRODUCED CAN BECOME STANDARD IN THIS WAY.

THERE ARE TWO SCHOOLS OF THOUGHT IN THE CURRENT DEBATE: ONE FOCUSES ON RESOURCE EFFICIENCY AND IMAGINES THAT, ON THIS BASIS, NONE OF THE HABITS OF MODERN LIFE NEED TO CHANGE. ITS ADVOCATES THINK IT'S ENOUGH TO SWITCH TO AN ELECTRIC SUV.

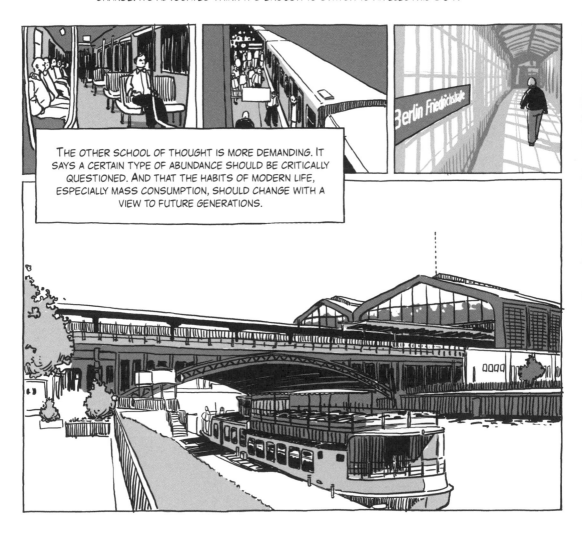

THE OTHER SCHOOL OF THOUGHT IS MORE DEMANDING. IT SAYS A CERTAIN TYPE OF ABUNDANCE SHOULD BE CRITICALLY QUESTIONED. AND THAT THE HABITS OF MODERN LIFE, ESPECIALLY MASS CONSUMPTION, SHOULD CHANGE WITH A VIEW TO FUTURE GENERATIONS.

The WBGU

In the age of Global Change, political decision-makers face the great challenge of having to take decisions even though the complex inter-relations between global environmental and development problems are not yet fully understood. For this reason, the German Federal Government set up the German Advisory Council on Global Change (WBGU) as an independent, scientific advisory body in 1992. Its main responsibilities are to analyse and report on global environmental and development problems, issue early warnings of new problem areas, prepare recommendations for action and research, and raise public awareness of global change issues.

The nine members of the WBGU meet for two days once a month to consider ways of moving towards global sustainable development. For example, they give recommendations on issues like how to move forward with the global energy-system transformation, how best to protect biodiversity, or how to achieve food security in a world with 9 billion people without destroying the environment. In addition to the nine Council members, the WBGU team also includes nine personal scientific research assistants to the Council members and a secretariat with extensive experience and excellent scientific expertise in the preparation and dissemination of reports. Once a report is finished, it is officially presented to the German Federal Government.

In 2011 the WBGU published a flagship report 'World in Transition – A Social Contract for Sustainability', which focused on the urgent need for the transformation to a low-carbon, sustainable society. In the report, the WBGU shows ways of accelerating such a trans-formation and presents ten packages of practical measures. This report became the basis of this book.

The WBGU is reappointed every four years. This guarantees a re-gular breath of fresh air and new ideas. The nine experts in this book were the WBGU Council members from 2008 to February 2013.

Dr Benno Pilardeaux
Head of Media and Public Relations,
WBGU Secretariat, Berlin

The publishers

Alexandra Hamann Alexandra Hamann is a media designer and has been running an educational media agency since 2001. She visualizes complex scientific and technological processes for teaching purposes. For several years she has been studying new ways of imparting knowledge. www.mintwissen.de

Claudia Zea-Schmidt is a communications scientist with Colombian roots. She began her working life in Berlin as a documentary film maker and correspondent for Deutsche Welle TV and Latin American channels. Since 2002 she has been developing and implementing projects for the print media, radio and television. Her passions are culture, science and politics. www.b26.info

Reinhold Leinfelder (see also page 124) is a member of the German Advisory Council on Global Change (WBGU) and one of the editors of this book. www.reinhold-leinfelder.de

Members of the WBGU

Professor Dr Dr hc Hans Joachim Schellnhuber is a physicist. He is the director of the Potsdam Institute for Climate Impact Research, a member of the Intergovernmental Panel on Climate Change (IPCC) and Chair of the WBGU. He is also Chair of the Governing Board of the Climate KICS (Knowledge and Innovation Community) of the European Institute for Technology. His research focuses on climate impact research and Earth system analysis.

Professor Dr Dirk Messner is a political scientist and economist. He is the director of the German Development Institute (DIE) in Bonn and co-director of the Centre for Advanced Studies on Global Cooperation Research at the University of Duisburg-Essen. Among other things, he studies the impact of climate change on global governance dynamics. He is Vice-Chair of the WBGU and advises not only the German Federal Government, but also the Chinese Government, the World Bank and the European Commission.

Professor Dr Reinhold Leinfelder is head of the department of Geobiology and Anthropocene Research at the Institute of Geological Sciences at Freie Universität Berlin, and Affiliated Carson Professor at the Rachel Carson Center for Environment and Society in Munich. He concentrates in particular on the fields of geobiology, biodiversity, Anthropocene research and science communication. He is especially interested in research on coral reefs.

Professor Dr Stefan Rahmstorf is head of the department of Earth System Analysis at the Potsdam Institute for Climate Impact Research and professor of physics of the oceans. His research concentrates primarily on the interactions between the oceans and global warming and on natural climate changes; he is a co-founder of the world-famous blogs RealClimate and KlimaLounge.

Professor Dr Jürgen Schmid is an aerospace engineer. Until 2012 he was director of the Fraunhofer Institute for Wind Energy and Energy System Technology (IWES) in Kassel. He is the founding president of the European Academy of Wind Energy (EAWE) and Chair of the Board of the Fraunhofer Institute for Solar Energy Supply Technology (ISET). Previously, he was head of the department of Efficient Energy Conversion at the University of Kassel. He co-invented the technology behind 'micromirror arrays' for directing light.

Professor Dr Nebojsa Nakicenovic is a systems analyst and professor of energy economics at the Technical University of Vienna. He is also deputy director general of the International Institute for Applied Systems Analysis (IIASA) in Laxenburg, Austria. Among other things he is engaged in research on economic development under the influence of climate change and on the evolution of energy, mobility, information and communication technologies.

Professor Dr Renate Schubert is an economist. She lectures in economics at the Swiss Federal Institute of Technology (ETH), Zurich, and is director of the ETH-based interdisciplinary Institute for Environmental Decisions, of which she was a founding member in 2005. She is engaged in research especially in the fields of decision-making, risk and insurance research, and energy and environmental economics.

Professor Dr Sabine Schlacke is a professor of law. She teaches public law with a focus on German, European and international environmental and administrative law at the University of Bremen and is the managing director of the Research Centre for European Environmental Law. She is also the publisher of the 'Zeitschrift für Umweltrecht' (Journal of Environmental Law).

Professor Dr Claus Leggewie is a political scientist. He is the director of the Institute for Advanced Studies in the Humanities (KWI) in Essen, and since 2012 co-director of the Centre for Global Cooperation Research ('Käte Hamburger Kolleg') on 'Political Cultures of World Society' at the University of Duisburg-Essen. His research focus is 'Climate Culture – the cultural prerequisites enabling modern societies to adapt to the effects of climate change.

The artists

Jörg Hülsmann, studied illustration in Düsseldorf and Hamburg. He works for a number of publishing houses and on independent projects. His book Die unsichtbaren Städte (The Invisible Cities), based on the novel by Italo Calvino, was selected as one of the ‚Best Designed German Books' by the Stiftung Buchkunst (Book Art Foundation). www.joerghuelsmann.de

Iris Ugurel, studied graphic art in Düsseldorf and Berlin, where she works as an artist and illustrator. Her works can be seen in numerous exhibitions. www.irisugurel.com.
Iris Ugurel and Jörg Hülsmann collaborate on projects and live in Berlin.

Studio Nippoldt
Graphic artist **Robert Nippoldt**, studied at the University of Applied Sciences Münster. His book 'Jazz – New York in the Roaring Twenties' was chosen as the 'Best Designed German Book of 2007'.
www.nippoldt.de

Illustrator **Christine Goppel**, studied visual communication at the Bauhaus University, Weimar. She illustrates, designs and writes books for children and adults. www.christinegoppel.de

Video artist **Astrid Nippoldt**, studied visual communication at the University of Applied Sciences Münster, and art at the University of the Arts in Bremen. Her works can be seen at international exhibitions. www.astridnippoldt.de

Jörg Hartmann, studied illustration and graphic design at the University of Applied Sciences in Münster and already began working for publishers as an illustrator as an undergraduate. In addition to illustrating children's books, he enjoys drawing comics (Wilsberg). www.extrakt.de

Glossary

Aerosol Tiny particles or droplets (e.g. pollen, dust, sulphur and other particles) that float in the air.

Africa-EU Energy Partnership Programme launched in 2007 aimed at promoting political cooperation between the EU and Africa in the energy sector, especially in ⇨ Renewable energies and energy efficiency.

Anocracy A form of government between ⇨ autocracy and democracy in which there are democratic procedures, but elites are nevertheless in power.

Anthropocene A term coined in 2000 by Paul Crutzen for a new geological era in which humanity's impact on the environment has reached a global dimension and can lead to significant changes in the ecosystems, including their destruction. One of the most important changes is climate change. In the 'Anthropocene', humans should see themselves not as an antipode to nature, but as part of it, in order to make sustainable economic activity possible.

Atmospheric window Spectral regions within which the atmosphere lets solar and terrestrial radiation (e.g. visible light, heat) through. They appear where the absorption of radiation by water vapour, ⇨ Carbon dioxide and ozone is particularly low.

Autocracy A form of government in which state authority is exercised by a single person or a group (party, central committee, junta). There is little or no provision for the participation of the population; examples include absolute monarchies and dictatorships.

Carbon One of the most common, naturally occurring elements and a basic building block of all organic life. Burns at higher temperatures to ⇨ Carbon dioxide, or to toxic carbon monoxide if the oxygen supply is insufficient.

Carbon cycle Cycle of ⇨ Carbon in its different forms and compounds (e.g. ⇨ Carbon dioxide) as it switches between the atmosphere, the land and the sea. Understanding of this cycle makes it possible, inter alia, to estimate the impact of humanity on the ⇨ Climate and on global warming.

Carbon dioxide/CO_2 Chemical compound comprising ⇨ Carbon and oxygen. An incombustible, acidic, colourless and odourless gas, readily soluble in water. It is a natural component of the air and a natural greenhouse gas that is produced or consumed in the organisms of living beings. The natural ⇨ Carbon cycle is a closed system. However, additional atmospheric carbon dioxide is created by the combustion of carbon-based substances, especially coal, crude oil and natural gas. Plants and some bacteria convert carbon dioxide into biomass. During photosynthesis, inorganic carbon dioxide and water are formed from glucose and other organic compounds.

Carbon sinks Everything that removes ⇨ Carbon dioxide from the atmosphere and stores the carbon over long periods (soil, ocean, plants, sediments, etc.).

The most important carbon sinks are the oceans and terrestrial ecosystems.

Centre for Advanced Studies on Global Cooperation Research Interdisciplinary centre for global cooperation research of the University of Duisburg-Essen. The Centre is a so-called Käte Hamburger Kolleg (Centre for Global Cooperation Research) (⇨ Rachel Carson Center). It regards global cooperation as key to effective and legitimate ways of processing urgent transnational problems.

Climate Climate is understood as the state of the climate system over a longer period of time. The climate system comprises, inter alia, the atmosphere, the ocean and the ice masses (the cryosphere).

Climate-KIC (Knowledge and Innovation Community) Research community launched in 2010 by the European Institute for Innovation and Technology (EIT). Its aim is to promote and accelerate the development of new technologies that help ameliorate the causes and consequences of climate change.

Combined heat and power (CHP) CHP systems permit an efficient use of fuels, since they not only generate electricity, but also use the waste heat that is also formed for heating (e.g. district heating) or in production processes that need heat.

Convection The transport of particles (e.g. air or water) by means of a current that is often caused by temperature differences (thermal convection).

Conservation International A non-profit organization founded in 1987 with the goal of conserving the global biodiversity of animals, plants and landscapes. The organization focuses primarily on areas with particularly high levels of biodiversity on land and in the sea and works mainly in Africa, Asia, Oceania and Central and South America.

Convention on Biological Diversity (CBD) An international environmental agreement negotiated in 1992 with the aim of protecting biodiversity (animal and plant species, genetic diversity within these species, ecosystems), using biodiversity sustainably, and achieving an equitable benefit sharing. This means, for example, that population groups who use traditional knowledge on the sustainable use of resources should be given a better share of its economic use. It is the first convention that deals with global nature conservation and species protection and aspires to sustainable development. It came into force in 1993 and has been signed by 168 states and the EU to date.

CO_2 ⇨ **Carbon dioxide**

Decarbonization The transition from the use of carbonaceous ⇨ Fossil fuels (esp. coal, crude oil, natural gas) to the use of ⇨ Renewable energies with zero CO_2 emissions.

Desertification The human-induced process of increasing land degradation in arid areas. This deterioration is primarily caused by the continuous overuse of natural resources (e.g. overgrazing, deforestation, false irrigation, unsuitable agriculture) in arid areas. The result is a decline in the vegetation, the erosion of the topsoil, the drying up of water reservoirs and even devastating dust storms.

Earth Summit in Rio de Janeiro ⇨ UN Conference on Environment and Development

Ecosystem service A term that looks at the benefits of ecosystems for humanity from the economic perspective. They include supply services (e.g. pollination of fruit blossom by bees, natural filtration of drinking water, reproduction of animals as food), regulating services (e.g. protection against flooding by alluvial forests), recreational services and support services (e.g. nutrient cycle).

Emerging economies Countries whose ongoing industrialization and successful economic development puts them on the threshold of becoming an 'industrialized country'. In some cases, their levels of literacy, infant mortality and life expectancy lag far behind their economic indicators.

Energiewende is the transformation of energy systems towards sustainability.

Evapotranspiration The evaporation of water from animals (mainly by sweating), plants (mainly by stomata in the leaves, transpiration) and from the surface of the soil.

Exajoule (EJ) ⇨ Joule

FAO (Food and Agriculture Organization of the United Nations) A specialized agency of the United Nations. It has the task of improving the production and distribution of agricultural products and foodstuffs worldwide, in order to secure the food supply and improve living standards.

Fossil energy carriers/resources/fuels Coal, crude oil and natural gas, which developed in the absence of oxygen from animals and plants that died millions of years ago.

Fracking (also known as hydraulic fracturing) A method of extracting oil and gas in which a liquid mixed with sand and chemicals is pumped under pressure into deep wells to create and widen cracks in the rock around the wells. This increases the permeability of the rock layer, so that "unconventional" natural gas and crude oil can be commercially extracted even from rocks that do not represent a conventional reservoir.

Fraunhofer Institute for Wind Energy and Energy System Technology (IWES) German research institute studying the entire spectrum of wind energy and the integration of ⇨ Renewable energies into supply structures.

German Development Institute (Deutsches Institut für Entwicklungspolitik, DIE) One of the world's leading research institutes on issues of global development and international development policy, operating in the fields of research, policy-advising work and training.

Gross domestic product (GDP) Value of all goods and services traded on the market that are produced in a year within the borders of a national economy. Germany's GDP includes what is produced by foreigners who work within the country; the output of Germans working abroad is not taken into account. The global GDP is the sum of all national GDPs.

Global 2000 Austria's leading independent environmental organization. It is a part of Friends of the Earth International and campaigns for an intact environment, a society that will remain viable in the future, and sustainable economic activity.

Great Transformation The term was coined as early as 1944 by the economist Karl Polanyi in an analysis of the Industrial Revolution in which he had studied the comprehensive transformation of national economies in interaction with the structures of the world economy. Drawing on Polanyi's understanding of transformation, the WBGU defines a great transformation towards a low-carbon, sustainable society as a comprehensive change involving a conversion of the national economies and the world economy within the ⇨ Planetary guard rails. The aim is to avoid not only irreversible damage to the Earth system and the ecosystems, but also the effects of this damage on humanity.

G-zero ⇨ G20

G20 Group of the most important industrialized countries and emerging economies plus the European Union. It serves as a forum for cooperation and consultations on the international financial system and was formed in 1999 as an informal group.

Institute for Advanced Studies in the Humanities (KWI) An interdisciplinary research institution for the humanities and social sciences based in Essen, Germany that examines modern culture. Research priorities currently include the culture of memory, interculturality, climate and culture, and the culture of responsibility.

Institute for Environmental Decisions (IED) The only research institute of its kind in Europe at the Swiss Federal Institute of Technology, Zurich (ETH). At the IED researchers from the fields of political science, psychology and economics examine the individual and collective decisions that are taken in the context of resource use and environmental problems.

Intergovernmental Panel on Climate Change (IPCC) Intergovernmental scientific institution studying climate change. The IPCC's main task is to describe the causes and effects of global warming and to compile strategies for prevention and adaptation. The IPCC does not engage in research itself, but compiles research findings from different disciplines, which it then publishes in 'assessment reports', pooling the results of hundreds of climate researchers from all over the world working in an honorary capacity. For over two decades, these reports have formed the basis of political and scientific discussions on climate change.

International Energy Agency (IEA) Cooperation platform founded in 1973 by 16 industrialized nations for the research, development, market launch and application of energy technologies. The Agency owns oil reserves with which it can intervene strategically in the oil market.

International Institute for Applied Systems Analysis (IIASA) engages in research in the fields of international politics and diplomacy, global strategies in environmental protection and new technologies – in international coordination with the UN, the ⇨ FAO and other organizations.

IPCC ⇨ Intergovernmental Panel on Climate Change

Joule Internationally binding physical unit for measuring energy: $1J = 1 kg * m^2/S^2$. 1 kilowatt-hour is equal to 3,600,000 joules.

Exajoule (EJ) 1 exajoule = 1018 joules = 1000 petajoules or 1 trillion joules

Petajoule (PJ) 1 petajoule = 1015 joules = 1 quadrillion joules

Kyoto Protocol An additional protocol adopted in 1997 to flesh out the ⇨ UN Framework Convention on Climate Change with the goal of protecting the climate. It was to come into force as soon as at least 55 countries – that together caused more than 55% of global CO_2 emissions in 1990 – had ratified the agreement. Since the USA, one of the largest emitters, today still refuses to accede to the Protocol, it did not become effective until early 2005 when it was ratified by Russia. For the first time, the agreement specified binding targets for greenhouse-gas emissions; it remains the only instrument of climate protection policy that is binding under international law. In 2012 the decision was taken to extend the Kyoto Protocol by another eight years. However, many industrialized countries have withdrawn from the treaty. The only remaining countries with commitments are the EU, Norway, Iceland, Liechtenstein, Switzerland, Monaco, Croatia, Ukraine, Belarus, Kazakhstan and Australia.

Latent heat The amount of heat needed to evaporate water. This amount of heat is released when water vapour condenses (i.e. when clouds form) and it is therefore an important source of heat in the atmosphere.

Net absorption of heat at the Earth's surface The difference between the heat absorbed by the Earth and the heat released by the Earth.

Net destruction of vegetation The difference between destroyed and newly developed vegetation.

Nitrogen cycle The migration and biogeochemical conversion of nitrogen in the Earth's atmosphere, lakes and oceans, soils and biomass. Nitrogen is essential to all living organisms. They absorb it from the environment when growing, and it is released again from the dead biomass after their death. Few plants or algae can absorb nitrogen directly from the atmosphere; most plants have to source nitrogen compounds from the soil, a process that can be intensified by fertilization. Animals and human beings, in turn, absorb nitrogen compounds via their food.

Ocean acidification The rising acidity of sea water, proven by measurements, caused by the absorption of ⇨ CO_2 from the air, because the CO_2 forms carbonic acid when it dissolves in water. Apart from global warming, the problem of ocean acidification is the main consequence of human-induced CO_2 emissions.

Peace Parks Foundation was founded by several states in southern Africa the 1997. It creates cross-border protection zones in order not only to conserve nature and culture, but also to promote and secure peaceful cooperation between neighbouring states.

Permafrost soils Soils that are frozen throughout the year. Most permafrost soils have been frozen since the last Ice Age. In Siberia the permafrost can reach depths of up to 1,500 m.

Petajoule (PJ) ⇨ Joule

Phosphorus cycle The constant migration and biogeochemical conversion of phosphorus in water, soil and biomass. Phosphorus is an essential mineral for all living things and occurs in different compounds. Without it there would be neither genetic material nor bones, neither leaves nor flowers. Outside of the biological cycle, phosphorus is a limited resource that is found only in a few regions of the world.

Planetary guard rails The WBGU developed the concept of planetary guard rails since 1995 and describes them as quantitatively definable damage thresholds, whose transgression either today or in future would have such intolerable consequences that even large-scale benefits in other areas could not compensate these. If the guard rails are complied with, the Earth system's functions, services and resources – essential for securing humankind's natural life-support systems and sustainable development – can be preserved. Avoiding ⇨ Tipping points in the Earth system – for example the irreversible melting of Greenland's ice sheet, the collapse of tropical coral reefs due to global warming, and other non-linear processes – plays a key role in setting the 2°C guard rail for climate protection. Compliance with the guard rails is a necessary, but not sufficient, criterion for ⇨ Sustainable development.

Potsdam Institute for Climate Impact Research (PIK) An interdisciplinary research centre established in 1992, which studies global climate change and its ecological, economic and social consequences, and designs strategies and options for a future-sustainable development of humankind and nature. The PIK is consulted not only by the Federal Government, but also by the European Commission and other national governments, as well as international organizations such as the World Bank. It is also constantly exchanging information and ideas with business and industry. Scientists from the PIK play an active role in the ⇨ Intergovernmental Panel on Climate Change.

ppm (parts per million) Unit for measuring the concentration of chemical substances. It shows, for example, the number of CO_2 molecules per 1 million gas molecules in the atmosphere.

Primary energy refers to naturally occurring energy before its loss-incurring conversion into usable energy, such as electricity. Primary energy carriers include e.g. lignite, coal, crude oil, natural gas and nuclear fuels. In the case of ⇨ Renewable energies such as wind and solar energy, the amount of electricity generated is often referred to as primary energy.

Pumped storage power station In a pumped storage power station, whenever power consumption is low, surplus electricity is used to pump water from a lower to an upper basin. When consumer demand for power is high, the upper basin is emptied, and the water flows back down to the lower basin, driving a turbine. The electricity generated in this way is fed back into the power grid.

Rachel Carson Center for Environment and Society (RCC) International interdisciplinary research and teaching centre in the field of environmental and social sciences. Part of the 'Käte Hamburger Kolleg' (⇨ Centre for Advanced Studies on Global Cooperation Research). The RCC was set up in 2009 by the Ludwig-Maximilians University, Munich, and the Deutsches Museum. It was named after the American biologist Rachel Carson (1907-1964), who is regarded as one of the founders of the modern environmental movement.

Rare earths Metals that are very important for many future technologies. They are used, inter alia, in the manufacture of wind turbines, light-emitting diodes, mobile phones and electric motors.

Rare earth metals include a total of 17 chemical elements. They are relatively common, but are only found in small quantities in the Earth's crust and need to be separated from various other minerals in a time-consuming process. This also creates toxic residues, with corresponding consequences for the environment.

Reinsurance Insurance companies sometimes have to make very large payouts to their customers, e.g. if they receive a lot of claims or there is a major damage event. To avoid financial ruin, they in turn take out an insurance policy with a reinsurer. Reinsurance companies have to assess long-term and large-scale risks and therefore invest heavily in climate research.

Renewable energy Energy from sustainable sources (sun, wind, water), which (in human dimensions) are inexhaustible. At the oppsite and of the scale are ⇨ Fossil fuels.

Renewable Energy Sources Act (EEG) The law on the primacy of ⇨ Renewable energy came into force in Germany on 1 April 2000. It guarantees sales of electricity at a fixed price to operators of power stations generating electricity from ⇨ Renewable energies.

Salinization An excessive accumulation of water-soluble salts in the soil. Naturally occurring groundwater or river water always contains a certain percentage of dissolved components, including salts. In arid areas, salinization is often caused by mistakes in irrigation. The dissolved salts enter the soil together with the water. When the water evaporates, the salts remain and gradually accumulate in the soil until the soil finally becomes too salty and barren. Excessive fertilization with mineral fertilizers can accelerate the process because, again, mineral salts accumulate by evaporation.

Santa Fe Institute A private, non-profit, community research and education centre founded in 1984 and based in Santa Fe, New Mexico, USA. It conducts interdisciplinary basic research in physics, biology, engineering and social sciences. Its work currently focuses on cognitive neuroscience, computer simulation in physics and life sciences, economic and social interactions, evolutionary dynamics and network dynamics.

Sedimentation The deposit of mineral or organic particles, e.g. on the ocean floor, the bottom of lakes or on land.

Spot price Term used in stock market trading. Price for the immediate procurement of an existing product; cash purchase price now.

Stratosphere The second layer of the Earth's atmosphere which begins at an altitude of about 8 km at the geographical poles and at approx. 18 km at the equator. Below it lies the troposphere, where most of the weather processes take place.

Super grid High-performance network for transporting electricity over long distances (often across continents). In high-voltage direct-current (HVDC) transmission, this is possible with little energy loss.

Sustainable Energy For All A global initiative launched UN Secretary-General Ban Ki-moon. It has three specific objectives to be achieved by 2030: unrestricted access for all to modern energy technologies worldwide; a 40% improvement in the productivity of ⇨ Renewable energies; and a 30% share of ⇨ Renewable energies in global energy use.

Sustainable development The classic definition of this concept comes from the Brundtland Report (Our Common Future), which was published in 1987 by the World Commission on Environment and Development: "Sustainable development is development that meets the needs of the present without compromising the ability of future generations to meet their own needs." Many other definitions exist in addition to this, all of which aspire to simultaneously drive forward economic, social and environmentally sustainable development.

Synergy Interaction of living organisms, substances or forces providing a common benefit.

Tipping elements Elements of the Earth system of supra-regional size that can 'tip over' into a completely different state, once a critical marginal value (⇨ Tipping point) is exceeded. This behaviour is based on self-reinforcing processes. Examples include the North Atlantic Current and ecosystems like the Amazon Forest.

Tipping point A critical point specific to a system at which, when crossed, a ⇨ Tipping element passes into a new state. For the Greenland Ice Sheet, for example, there is a critical temperature above which a vicious circle begins in which the ice melts completely.

TWh/terawatt hour Corresponds to 1,000,000,000 kWh: enough energy to cook a midday meal for about a billion people on an electric stove, or to supply 285,000 households with electricity for a year (assuming a power consumption of 3,500 kWh per year).

United Nations Conference on Sustainable Development (UNCSD or Rio+20) Took place in Rio de Janeiro in 2012 to mark the 20th anniversary of the 1992 United Nations Conference on Environment and Development (UNCED). The Conference focused on two themes: (a) a green economy in the context of sustainable development and poverty eradication; and (b) the institutional framework for sustainable development.

United Nations Framework Convention on Climate Change (UNFCCC) International environmental agreement with the aim of stabilizing the concentration of greenhouse gases in the atmosphere enough to prevent dangerous anthropogenic interference with the climate system. The convention was adopted at the 1992 ⇨ United Nations Conference on Environment and Development and came into force in March 1994. In the meantime it has been ratified by more than 190 states, including the countries with the biggest greenhouse-gas emissions: USA, Russia, European Union, China and India. The UNFCCC itself does not contain any specific commitments to protect the climate; these were laid down (only for the industrialized countries) in the ⇨ Kyoto Protocol.

United Nations Conference on Environment and Development (UNCED) (also called the Rio Earth Summit) Held in Rio de Janeiro in 1992, where the ⇨ UNFCCC, the ⇨ Convention on Biological Diversity and the ⇨ United Nations Convention to Combat Desertification were adopted. The conference is regarded as a milestone in global sustainability policy. The right to ⇨ Sustainable development as a global model for the 21st century was enshrined in the Rio Declaration on Environment and Development for the first time: "Human beings are at the centre of concerns for sustainable development. They are entitled to a healthy and productive life in harmony with nature. (...) The right to development must be fulfilled so as to equitably meet developmental and environmental needs of present and future generations" (Principles 1 and 3 of the Declaration).

United Nations Convention to Combat Desertification (UNCCD) Established in 1994, UNCCD is the sole legally binding international agreement linking environment and development to sustainable land management. The Convention addresses specifically the arid, semi-arid and dry sub-humid areas, known as the drylands. In the 10-Year Strategy of the UNCCD (2008-2018) that was adopted in 2007, Parties to the Convention further specified their goals: "to forge a global partnership to reverse and prevent desertification/land degradation and to mitigate the effects of drought in affected areas in order to support poverty reduction and environmental sustainability". The UNCCD has been ratified by 195 countries.

US 48 Also known as Continental USA. The 48 US states on the North American continent that share land borders. It does not include Alaska, Hawaii or the American Overseas Territories.

Water scarcity

> **Physical water scarcity** More than 75% of the water is taken from rivers (particularly in Central Asia, southern India, North Africa, the Middle East and in the west of the USA).

> **Emerging physical water scarcity** More than 60% of river water is taken.

> **Economic water scarcity** There would be enough water to meet human needs (less than 25% of the water is taken from rivers), but the necessary investments are not being made to give people access to water (primarily in Africa, South Asia, South America).

WBGU (German Advisory Council on Global Change) See page 122

Weather The short-term conditions in the atmosphere in a specific area. In contrast to the development of the climate, weather conditions are greatly influenced by random processes and can only be forecast over short periods.

World Resources Institute (WRI) A non-profit organization based in Washington D.C. that collaborates internationally with governments, business and civil society to protect the environment, promote ⇨ Sustainable development and improve people's living conditions. More than 100 business analysts, economists, political experts and other scientists work at the WRI.

WWF (World Wide Fund for Nature) One of the largest international nature-conservation organizations. It was founded in 1961 as the World Wildlife Fund in Switzerland.

References

p. 18 Planetary Boundaries. From: Rockström, J. et al.: „A safe operating space for humanity". In: Nature 461, 2009. See also: http://www.nature.com/nature/journal/v461/n7263/fig_tab/461472a_F1.html#figure-title

p. 28 Meat Production. Source: Keeping Track of Our Changing Environment: From Rio to Rio+20 (1992-2012). Division of Early Warning and Assessment (DEWA), United Nations Environment Programme (UNEP), Nairobi, 2011. See also: http://www.unep.org/geo/pdfs/Keeping_Track.pdf

p. 30 Oil and Gas Deposits. Source: The Association for the Study of Peak Oil and Gas (ASPO), Newsletter No. 38, Februar 2004. See also: http://www.peakoil.net/Newsletter/NL38/Newsletter38.html

p. 32 Water Scarcity. Source: UNESCO: The 3rd United Nations World Water Development Report: Water in a Changing World, 2009. See also: http://webworld.unesco.org/water/wwap/wwdr/wwdr3/pdf/WWDR3_Water_in_a_Changing_World.pdf

p. 33 Death Zones are Formed. From: Dan Swenson in The Times Picayune 2007. See also: http://blog.nola.com/times-picayune/2007/06/despite_promises_to_fix_it_the.html

p. 33 Death Zones in Europe. See: http://earthobservatory.nasa.gov/IOTD/view.php?id=44677

p. 35 Tipping Points in a Coral Reef. Graphic: Reinhold Leinfelder 2012.

p. 38 Carbon Cycle. Source: German Advisory Council on Global Change (WBGU). See also http://www.wbgu.de/uploads/media/4.1-1.jpg

p. 38 Greenhouse Effect. From: Kevin E. Trenberth, John T. Fasullo and Jeffrey Kiehl: „Earth's global Energy budget". In: Bulletin of the American Meteorological Society, 2008. See also: http://www.cgd.ucar.edu/cas/Trenberth/trenberth.papers/10.1175_2008BAMS2634.1.pdf. Data: IPCC 2007.

p. 39 Global Mean Temperature. From: Malte Meinshausen et al.: „Greenhouse-gas emission targets for limiting global warming to 2 °C", in: Nature 458, 2009. See also: http://www.iac.ethz.ch/people/knuttir/papers/meinshausen09nat.pdf

p. 40 Global Warming. Source: International Panel on Climate Change (IPCC): Fourth Assessment Report: Climate Change, 2007. See also: http://www.ipcc.ch/publications_and_data/ar4/wg1/en/figure-spm-6.html

p. 42 Coastal Deltas. Source: IPCC: Fourth Assessment Report: Climate Change, 2007. See also: http://www.ipcc.ch/publications_and_data/ar4/wg2/en/xccsc3.html

p. 43 Sea Level. From: Andrew C. Kemp et al.: Climate related sea-level variations over the past two millennia, PNAS 2011. See also: http://www.pik-potsdam.de/sealevel/en/images.html

p. 50 World Population. Source: Population Division of the Department of Economic and Social Affairs of the United Nations Secretariat: World Population Prospects: The 2010 Revision. See also: http://esa.un.org/unpd/wpp/index.htm und http://www.un.org/esa/population/publications/sixbillion/sixbillion.htm

p. 51 Emerging Economies: From: Die ZEIT, no. 22, 21.5.2008.

p. 56 Peace Parks: From: http://www.tfpd.co.za

p. 62 Renewable Energy. Source: WBGU: World in Transition. A Social Contract for Sustainability, Berlin, 2011.

p. 63 Pumped Storage Power Stations. From: http://www.pskw.at/pumpspeicher-kraftwerk/funktionsprinzip

p. 63 Natural gas from eco-electricity. From: Arbeitsgemeinschaft für sparsamen und umweltfreundlichen Energieverbrauch e. V. (ASUE). See also: http://asue.de/themen/umwelt----klimaschutz/grafiken/grafik_oekostrom_04.html

p. 70 Offshore Wind Platform. From: Thomas L. Lee of Stanbury Resources. Inc.

p. 70 Airborne Wind Turbine. From: Altaeros Energies. See also: http://www.altaerosenergies.com

p. 70 Wind Kites. From: Stanford Report 2009. See also: http://news.stanford.edu/news/2009/june24/high-altitude-winds-062309.html

p. 73 Sahara. Source: Greenpeace. See also: www.greenpeace.de/themen/energie/nachrichten/artikel/400_milliarden_euro_fuer_wuestenstrom_kraftwerke/ansicht/bild

p. 74 Global Primary Energies. From: Riahi, K. et al.: Global Energy Assessment. Towards a Sustainable Future, International Institute for Applied Systems Analysis (IIASA) 2012. See also: http://www. sustainableenergyforall.org/component/k2/item/download/ 46_60ad99d05ed07e6c49cff5eb02d2c967

p. 76 Maglev Route. From: Yoshiki Yamagata, National Institute for Environmental Studies Japan (NIES) 2010. See also: http://www.nies.go.jp

p. 76 Tubes. From: Paul Michael Grant, Electric Power Research Institute (EPRI) 2010. See also: http://my.epri.com

p. 79 Consumption of Animal-based Foods. From: McMichael, A. J. et al. „Food, livestock production, energy, climate change and health". In: The Lancet, 370, 2007.

p. 79 Land Required. From: Atsuko Wakamiya: „Wie viel Fläche braucht ein Mensch um sich zu ernähren?". In: Ökologie & Landbau 159, 2011.

p. 82 Urbanization. Source: Grübler, A. et al.: „Urban Energy Systems." In: Riahi, K. et al.: Global Energy Assessment. Towards a Sustainable Future, International Institute for Applied Systems Analysis (IIASA) 2012.

p. 82 Higher Education. Source: W. Lutz, A. Goujon, p. K.C. and W. Sanderson: Reconstruction of populations by age, sex and level of educational attainment for 120 countries for 1970-2000. Vienna Yearbook of Population Research 2007, p. 193-235.

p. 82 Democratization. Source: G. Modelski, T. Devezas and W. R. Thompson (Hrsg.): Globalization as Evolutionary Process — Modeling Global Change. Routledge, Abingdon 2008.

p. 82 Autocracies. From: Monty G. Marshall, Benjamin R. Cole: Global Report 2009. Conflict, Governance, and State Fragility. Center for Systemic Peace, Center for Global Policy, 2009. See also: http://www. systemicpeace.org/Global%20Report%202009.pdf

p. 86 Investments. Source: International Energy Agency (IEA) 2010 from WBGU 2011.

p. 89 Natural Disasters. Source: Munich Re: Topics Geo. Naturkatastrophen 2011. Analysen, Bewertungen, Positionen, 2012. See also: http://www.munichre.com/publications/302-07224_de.pdf

p. 91 Investments by Countries and Industries. Source: McKinsey 2009 from WBGU 2011.

p. 92 Gross Power Generation. Data: AG Energiebilanzen e. V. (AGEB).

p. 93 Global Foreign Exchange Reserves. Source: World Gold Council, Bloomberg.

p. 94 Import Dependency. Source: AG Energiebilanzen e. V. (AGEB).

p. 95 Jobs by Industry. Data: DLR/DIW/ZSW/GWS/Prognos 2012.

p. 99 Renewable Energy. Data: Bundesverband der Energie- und Wasserwirtschaft e.V. (BDEW): Energie. Wasser. Leben, 2012. See also: https://eco.ms/go/z9edl

p. 100 Material Cycle. From: European Environment Agency (EEA): The European Environment State and Outlook (SOER) 2010. Material Resources and Waste. See also: http://www.eea.europa.eu/soer/europe/ material-resources-and-waste

p. 102 Price decline for CO_2. From: Frankfurter Allgemeine Zeitung of 17.4.2012. See also: http://www.faz. net/aktuell/wirtschaft/wirtschaftspolitik/klimaschutz-der-co2-ausstoss-wird-billig-11719914.html

p. 104 Kyoto Targets. Source: Bundeszentrale für politische Bildung. See also: http://www.bpb.de/ nachschlagen/zahlen-und-fakten/globalisierung/52817/internationale-vertraege

p. 105 Investment in Renewable Energy. Source: UNEP: Global Trends in Renewable Energy Investment, 2011. See also: http://fs-unep-centre.org/publications/global-trends-renewable-energy-investment-2011

p. 107 India. Source: Government of India Ministry of New and Renewable Energy (MNRE), Annual Report 2006-2007.

p. 112 Assessment of Climate Change. Source: World Values Survey 2009 from WBGU 2011.

p. 113 Quality of Life. Source: Bertelsmann-Stiftung 2010 from WBGU 2011.

p. 115 Changing Values. Source: Eurobarometer 2007 from WBGU 2011.